THE CHORD OF STEEL

The Chord of Steel

The Story of the Invention
of the Telephone

THOMAS B. COSTAIN

Doubleday & Company, Inc., Garden City, New York

1960

Library of Congress Catalog Card Number 60–10085

Foreword

THIS is not the full story of the invention of the telephone; nor is it, in any sense, a biography of Alexander Graham Bell. My sole purpose has been to tell of a few eventful years which began with the arrival of the Bell family in Brantford, Ontario, and the purchase of their home on a bend of the Grand River called Tutelo Heights, and which ended when the son of the family demonstrated by three remarkably successful tests that the human voice could be heard, clearly and understandably, after traveling over miles of telegraph wire. Brantford's part in the invention ended there.

My reason for telling the story again is that the world at large has had little chance to learn all that took place in that very important span of time. Driving through the Ontario city, and seeing the splendid monument erected there to commemorate the event, people are too often puzzled and surprised. They are prone to say, "But the telephone was invented in Boston." A motion picture was made about the remarkable young Scot and the miracle he achieved, in which there was no mention, if my memory serves me right, of Brantford. A travelogue of Canada included a shot of the monument but then proceeded to defeat its own purpose by calling the city

Brentwood; a mistake which has been repeated in at least one article since.

Alexander Graham Bell has said that the telephone was the work of many men and that the invention will never be completed. The part of this most modest of men was in the inception of the great idea and the devising of instruments which made it possible for people to speak to each other over steel wires. The perfecting and extension of the system followed, perhaps as a matter of course, but he was most generous in thus paying tribute to the magnificent developments which have been brought about in three-quarters of a century. The actual invention was, in reality, a tale of two cities, Brantford and Boston. In setting it down, I have striven to be impartial and to describe the results of the Bell experiments in Boston, particularly the all-important discovery of the undulating current. My primary aim, however, has been to demonstrate that Brantford's share in the great achievement has been overshadowed if not overlooked, and to tell what happened in fuller detail, perhaps, than ever before.

In order to forestall criticism, I should explain that I changed the spelling of the Heights from the "Tutela," which is now used, to the original "Tutelo." Graham Bell and his father, Alexander Melville Bell, were convinced that "Tutelo" was the correct form of the word and they made efforts to get the fact recognized.

I have many to thank for help in completing this rather difficult piece of narration. First, I desire to express my gratitude to Mr. George L. Long, historian of the Bell Telephone Company of Canada, who has been of so much assistance that I rather think he should have been named a co-author; and his associates and his staff in Montreal. Mr. Long supplied me with much original material and photographs and he corrected the errors into which my lack of technical knowledge led me. Of the greatest importance also has been the help of Miss Marjorie Jordan, who comes from Brantford, and who did what might be termed the "field work" for me, interviewing people who had information to give about the Great Event and supplying me with reams of the most valuable notes. Also, I benefited from the ever ready cooperation of Mr. Cyril Sanders of the Brantford *Expositor*.

I desire to extend my thanks to a rather considerable list of people, mostly from Brantford, who contributed useful side lights. Among them are Mr. George Nelson, Toronto, vice-president of Doubleday in Canada, Mr. Harold Hill and Miss Shields and Miss Goode of the Brant County Historical Society, Mr. William H. Brooks and Mr. George M. Ballachey, who are, I believe, the sole surviving witnesses, Miss Margaret Smyth and Mr. George Cooke of Mount Pleasant, Miss Gladys Steuart-Jones of Paris and the editors of the Paris *Star*, Mrs. W. H. Waldie, Dr. James H. Moyle, Mrs. R. V. Wolfindin, Mr. Frank Calbeck, Mrs. Harry Hewitt, Mr. G. E. F. Sweet, Mr. J. A. D. Slemin, Mrs. R. L. Houlding, and Miss Joyce King of the Brantford Library.

I found Catherine Mackenzie's biography of Alexander Graham Bell most helpful.

Finally, I desire to say that it was my wife who suggested the book. She pointed out to me that someone ought to do it and that, as I was born and raised in Brantford, I should perhaps assume the task myself. She gave me, moreover, the encouragement I needed when my energy flagged and when I complained, as I often did, of the difficulties I was encountering.

CONTENTS

9

CONTENTS

THE CHORD OF STEEL

Chapter One

The Bell Family
Comes to Brantford

1

MY pencil almost slipped into the error of saying it was on a lazy afternoon in August 1870 that a light phaeton, which, if it were still in existence, would be preserved with zealous care in a museum, drove down one of the main streets in Brantford, a small city in the province of Ontario, Canada. It could not have been a lazy afternoon. There was no indolence of pace about the city and the air was always as brisk as the habits of the people.

I was always wakened by the whistles and bells stridently summoning men to work. First there would be the arrogant clangor from the Massey-Harris, Waterous, Cockshutt, and Verity plants, the distinctive "buzz" which called carpenters to their labors at Schultz Brothers vying with the ringing of the iron bell at Buck's Foundry, and finally, because it came from a distance, what seemed a laggard call from Slingsby's. In later years, as a reporter in my home town, I found it necessary to hustle about my work and it seemed to me then that everyone else was moving with equal energy and purpose.

No, there has never been anything lazy about Brantford; and so I am inclined to think that the horse drawing this particular conveyance down Brant Avenue came along at a good rate of speed, making its hoofs sound a fine round clip-clop on the hard dirt surface of the road. Seated in the phaeton were two ladies and two men. One of the ladies was of middle age and had an air of refinement and a quiet charm which might have seemed familiar to readers of Jane Austen novels. The other was young and dressed with a hint of recent bereavement. The older of the two men had a beard which showed some traces of gray in its almost patriarchal length. The younger, who seemed in his quite early twenties, also had a beard: black, and carefully trimmed, and with the sparseness and gloss of youth. The elder wore a tall hat of gray beaver, the younger man a tweed cap.

Among the stories still told in Brantford about the coming of the Bell family, one concerns two citizens who happened to be standing together at the corner of Brant Avenue and Church Street when the dusty phaeton drove by. "There they are," said one of them, who could be identified as a doctor by the tip of a stethoscope protruding from his vest pocket. "Did you see the item about them in the *Expositor*?"

The second man, who was in the real estate business, nodded briskly. "Name's Bell. I heard this morning they've bought the Morton property on Tutelo Heights."

"Away out there? Isn't that odd?"

"I certainly thought so. There were good properties on my list would have suited them. Right here on Brant Avenue and over on Dufferin. They paid a good price, too, I hear."

"How much?"

"Two thousand six hundred dollars. It goes to show. Values are picking up in Brantford."

"I've heard something or other about his family," said the doctor. "The father was well known in England. A scientist, I think."

The real estate man nodded his head with the satisfaction which accompanies the possession of precise information. "He's a real professor. Gives lectures around the country. On deafness. He knows how to read lips, so I hear."

The phaeton passed on and vanished from sight down the grade leading to the downtown bridge. The doctor shook his head thoughtfully. "It seems to me," he said, "that the young fellow looked kind of peaked. As though he might have a touch of lung trouble."

The trained medical eye had not been at fault. It was because of a weakness in the lungs of his sole surviving son that Alexander Melville Bell had given up his lucra-

tive post in London and had come out to settle in Brantford. The section known as Tutelo Heights on the high
circular bluff around which the Grand River coils on its
way to Lake Erie had been selected because the atmosphere there seemed particularly fresh and invigorating.

2

The carriage with the Bell family crossed over the river
at the foot of Brant Avenue on a temporary bridge soon
to be replaced by one which lasted for many years and
would be called the Iron Bridge. They found themselves
in a section known as West Brantford. Turning onto the
Mount Pleasant Road, they began a gradual ascent.
After passing Farringdon Church, they made a left turn
onto the Tutelo Heights Road, which followed in narrow
dustiness the line of the river bluffs.

This had been part of the Indian grant, and all the
land along the bluffs had once belonged to a man named
Stewart because he had taken unto himself an Indian
wife, obviously a chief's daughter. The Stewart holdings
had gradually been sold and at this time there were a
number of comfortable houses along the opposite side
of the road from the water; the McIntyre house, the
white stone home of Thomas Brooks, and the Edward
Blacker place. Farther down, where the road took a
sharp turn to the left, lay Grove Park Farm, where Ig-
natius Cockshutt, one of the leading citizens, had built
an expensive home in a cover of trees which screened it

partially from view. All beyond this was Cockshutt domain. The Cockshutt Road crossed the river farther down at the Cockshutt Bridge, and most of the land thereabouts belonged to members of the family.

The property which Professor Bell had purchased was the second between the road and the river. The ladies of the family, seeing it for the first time, found it an engaging prospect. The house stood well back from the road and was screened by tall trees and thick green shrubs; a two-story structure of quaint charm, with white walls and black trim, an ornate but not unattractive porch stretching across most of the front. To the right, as seen from the road, was a conservatory, which in the esteem of most people gave quite an air to the place.

"Melville House," said the new owner, climbing out of the phaeton and surveying his domain with a proper pride. He looked rather stout in his double-breasted frock coat, an effect heightened by the fullness of his beard.

His quiet wife, who had been looking about her with quickly inquiring eyes, read from his lips what he had said. She smiled in acquiescence; and Melville House it remained, until the time came when the extraordinary success of their son made another name, a prouder one, more suitable.

Mrs. Bell was very well dressed. To a feminine eye she would have seemed stylish (the highest praise possible) in a traveling suit of shot velvet, of a brown shade called cuir. Although she conformed to the standards of the day in the matter of a bustle and a fullness of skirt, she succeeded in looking slender and even delicate.

Their daughter-in-law, the widow of the oldest of the three Bell sons, was in black and seemed somewhat subdued in mood. Her straw bonnet, which she wore tilted forward, was nevertheless small and pretty.

The inside of the house was as charming as the exterior. The high-ceilinged hall had a stairway at the back with a graceful rail. To the right was a long parlor with a fireplace and a tall french window opening on the porch. Behind this was a small room which would serve them as a study. Still further to the right, behind the conservatory, was a room which was taken over later as a workshop, and which, perhaps, should be counted the most important part of the house. Here also, tucked into a corner, was a small bathroom with a newly installed tub, a rather tinny affair but quite smart for that day.

To the left of the hall was a sitting room, also with a fireplace and a french window, and behind that a dining room with a hatch in the wall opening out to the pantry. Back of the kitchen was a room on the order of a summer kitchen. There were four bedrooms above with a central hall. Some doubts exist now as to how they were apportioned, but the general opinion seems to be that the soon to be famous son occupied the rear room to the right.

A rather rambling place, a little perhaps like Bleak House (in a very small way) but a comfortable one. Unlike the home of Mr. Jarndyce, the east wind would seldom be felt here while the Bell family was in possession.

While the ladies went on a minute tour of inspection of the house, the two men walked back toward the river through the orchard.

"A first dividend on our investment" was the thought in the mind of the head of the family as his eyes took in the ample crop of apples, pears, and plums.

The typical Scot seldom showed in the men of the family. There was nothing dour or stern about them. In fact, there was a hint of the actor instead, a mobility of expression, a slight puckishness about the corners of the eyes. They laughed a great deal and frowned seldom. There was much of the thespian in the head of the family when he spread out both arms on reaching the edge of the deep slope down to the river.

The real estate men who sold them the property had claimed, characteristically, that Tutelo Heights was almost on a par with the Plains of Abraham. But as Melville Bell talked, every word he said could have been heard on the water below and perhaps even from the opposite bank; so strong and round was his voice.

There was perhaps more of the poet than the actor in the son. He was looking about him with a new sense of inner satisfaction. The bluffs above the water were steep and high. To the north, the river looped and twisted several times before passing out of sight under the spires and factory chimneys of Brantford. To the south the heights took a sharp circular turn and then tapered down to the flat expanse of farm lands known as Bow Park. The soil of part of the slope was as bare as a newly turned furrow, giving the impression that the cutting of the channel had been a recent labor of the Grand.

"Not as fine as the view from Arthur's Seat," thought the father.

The son drew his breath in deep draughts, for he was finding the air stimulating and good. Perhaps this new home would provide the salvation for him that they were seeking. He had seen his two brothers die of the disease which accounted for his own slenderness of frame and the trace of high color in his cheeks. It had seemed a doubtful gamble to him when they started on their long sea voyage. When he sang at the ship's concert "Will Ye No Come Back Again," accompanying himself on the piano, it had been of his own plight he had been thinking and not of the departure from Scotland of Bonnie Prince Charlie. The other passengers had been carried away by the intensity of the feeling he had put into the old song and had applauded enthusiastically.

Here, so isolated and high, with a cool breeze blowing off the river, he might get his health back. For the first time, perhaps, he felt really hopeful.

His father pointed to the line of tall trees along the brink and selected one spot where the space between two poplars was just the right width for a hammock.

A few feet beneath this, scooped out of the sloping earth, was a hole of quite considerable size, large enough for a tall man to stretch himself out at full length. This would be put to good and frequent use, with the aid of pillows and a horse blanket, and would be called by the members of the family the "sofa seat."

Young Aleck Bell had already seen other uses for these shady places where the full benefit of the breeze could be enjoyed. Even during his most doubtful moments, when he had secretly feared that he must soon follow his brothers to the grave, his mind had been full of plans, of theories, of half formulated beliefs in the possibility of making an extraordinary new use of sound. Yes, he said to himself, this was an ideal place to rest, but it was more than that. It was a perfect place to reflect and study and plan.

Chapter Two

The Three Alexanders

1

I T is most unusual for all the members of a family to share one interest and for this mutual absorption to continue through three generations. This was true of the Bell family, who devoted their lives to the training of the human voice

It began with Alexander Bell, the grandfather, who was a shoemaker at St. Andrews, Scotland, in the early years of the nineteenth century. The game of golf was in such an early stage at this time that it could scarcely be said to have any existence at all; except at St. Andrews, where the Ancient and Honourable Golf Club had been active for half a century. With so much walking over the stony banks and braes, the shoes of the members wore out more quickly than usual and so the trade of a shoemaker should have been highly remunerative. But the first Aleck Bell had a far different ambition from that of fashioning shoes for golfers. He wanted to be an actor.

He had a fine presence for the stage, although he was not tall. His forehead was broad and high and surrounded by close, curling hair. His eyes reflected every emotion which took possession of him, his nose was substantial (which remained a feature of the family), and his mouth eloquent. Unfortunately the stage was regarded not only as "low" in Scotland but downright wicked. Handsome young Mr. Bell, who had married into a substantial family, the Colvills, encountered serious opposition to his plan. He did the next best thing. He moved to Edinburgh and set himself up as a teacher in speech and elocution.

Proving successful, as well, as a Shakespearean reader, he published a textbook called *Elegant Extracts*, which became very popular; it being considered proper to read the plays of the immortal bard or even to hear them read in public, but under no circumstances to see them played on the stage!

Some years later he opened a school for boys at Dundee and this proved so successful that the family had a carriage of their own, which was a proof of very considerable affluence. Finally he moved to London and purchased a house on Harrington Square. The aura of aristocracy did not hang low over this particular square, but people in London spoke of it as "nobby," a term well deserved.

The teaching of elocution proved so profitable that Alexander the First lived here in luxury and ease.

2

The thwarted actor in Alexander the First came out in all his children, particularly in his second son, who was born in Edinburgh in 1819 and given the name of Alexander Melville. When in his early youth he was sent to Newfoundland for his health, he took advantage of a chance, first to organize a Shakespeare class and then to start the members on amateur theatricals. He acted as director but it is probable he managed to insinuate himself into some of the humble bit parts with which Shakespeare's plays abound. There did not seem to be any shortage of theatrical talent, but finding costumes was a different matter. His experience as an actor was destined to begin and end there, but he managed to establish one histrionic record even in so short a time. His Antony appeared on the stage wearing cavalry boots!

It was while in Newfoundland that he gained a respect for the fresh airs of the American continent which resulted later in his moving there. Newfoundland was not the dark and dismal place he had expected, covered with heavy clouds and with fogs which outdid those of London. Against the clear blue of the sky the mountain peaks stood up straight and high, and only in the direction of the Banks, a hundred miles out to sea, did there seem to be continuously foggy weather. He liked the island so much that he was sorry when it became necessary to leave and he talked often thereafter of going back.

The second Alexander Bell inherited the family traits and talents in superabundance. He was destined to reduce the teaching of proper speech to a science and to write a book called *Bells Standard Elocutionist*, which came out in 1860 and has continued to sell ever since. The number of editions through which it has run approaches now the monumental number of two hundred. He was to be also the inventor of a system which he called Visible Speech, about which much will be told later.

He was a man of powerful presence. His voice, due to his own self-imposed training and discipline, was deep and resonant, without a trace of accent or burr. In platform readings from Shakespeare, he let his suppressed desire to be an actor take possession of him and his audiences would hang upon every word. He was almost as successful as Charles Dickens would become later, when he took to reading extracts from his novels in public. And the mention of that great author and showman brings up an amusing incident in the early life of the second Alexander Bell. Finding his audiences so receptive to Shakespeare, he decided to provide diversity by inserting some light pieces from Dickens. The elders of the church which he attended were furious that he had descended to the frivolity of Sam Weller and Mr. Pickwick and they created such a disturbance about it that the elocutionist resigned his membership.

The turning point in the life of Alexander the Second came when he left London (where he had been assisting his father) for Edinburgh in preparation for a second trip across the Atlantic. This was in 1843 and there was in the Scottish capital at the time a painter of miniatures, a Miss Eliza Grace Symonds, who had developed a wide clientele. It occurred to young Bell that he should get himself immortalized on ivory before leaving for the wilds of America, so he sat to Miss Symonds for his portrait in water color.

The artist seems to have been sufficiently interested in this dynamic young man to call upon her full resources. At any rate she produced an inspired likeness. Here was a young man who was going to cut a swath in the world: a fine mop of black hair brushed back carelessly from a white forehead, a pair of dark eyes looking out eagerly at life, the merest hint of the maturity of whiskers on each cheek, the well-modeled Bell nose. He was, moreover, attired most stylishly in the best Early Victorian tradition, a coat with wide black lapels, a dark silk tie knotted under a high white collar, the glove stripped modishly from one hand and held in the other.

Well, they were married soon after and the eager subject of the portrait gave up the idea of returning to America. They settled down in Edinburgh in a flat at 16 South Charlotte Street, a rather dark habitation up several flights of stairs. Young Bell gave himself out as a professor of elocution and the art of speech and began to collect pupils. In addition, he continued his readings from Shakespeare. Mrs. Bell went on with her career as a portrait painter. If her work is to be judged by the one she had done of her husband and a self-portrait, she had a most unusual degree of talent. The self-portrait seems unsparing and perhaps unfair compared with the painting of her by H. Ulke which hangs today in the homestead at Tutelo Heights. In the Ulke painting, which poses her in partial profile, she has both beauty and charm in a much greater degree than she has allowed herself. The miniature nonetheless is a masterpiece of detail. The lace at her neck and wrists, and the fabric of a dark lace jacket are done with meticulous artistry.

They had three children, all boys. The second, named Alexander, was born on March 3, 1847, which as it happened was his grandfather's birthday. Soon after his arrival the parents moved to a lighter domicile at 13 South Charlotte Street and it was here that he was raised. It was sufficiently large for the family to be comfortable and Mrs. Bell had adequate domestic help. In addition, her widowed mother lived in the same house in an upper flat.

The oldest of their three sons, who was christened Melville James, had inherited the histrionic gifts of his father and grandfather. His capacity for mimicry, in fact, was so great that he could deliver monologues in the course of which his dark and expressive features would take on the guise of any number of successive characters. His voice was an instrument of such pliability that he could change it at will. He had it in him to become the great comedian his grandfather had wanted to be, a Grossmith, a Martyn Green. In addition, he could perform tricks of magic with such skill that his audiences were always baffled.

The second son will monopolize nearly all the pages which follow and so it does not seem necessary to refer to him further at this point.

The third son, named Edward Charles, was born on September 20, 1848. He seems to have been a quiet and gentle boy, of an artistic temperament. The letters he sent his parents were always embellished with sketches of people he had seen and things which had happened. They showed a real gift for caricature, and it is unfortunate that they seemed to have been lost in the passage of the years. The third boy was always a little delicate and he grew rapidly, finally reaching the unusual height of six feet four inches.

Because he was not strong, the two older brothers were always very solicitous of "little Edward." They kept watchful eyes on him, sparing him discomfort and guarding him in every way. A diary kept by Alexander, now alas lost, had many references to this rather diffident but gifted younger brother, in all of which a deep affection was displayed.

3

Alexander the Third, or perhaps it would be more to the point to call him Alexander the Great, was a Bell in many respects but in the most important aspect he went far beyond the others. To the rest of the family the teaching of proper speech was an end in itself. To the third of the line it was no more than a means to an end. In addition to his share in the family preoccupation, he was perhaps more deeply interested than the rest in music, art, and poetry. But the point of drastic departure was that his mind, even as a boy, had begun to explore the dim and far removed lanes of science.

This interest was instinctive and in no sense a result of his education. Mrs. Bell undertook the teaching of her three sons and it is certain she made no effort to open their eyes to the strange and hidden forces which govern the world. Had she done so, she would have been a real pioneer; for the schools of the day had not come to recognize science in any of its branches as a compulsory subject. She taught them regularly at home and even continued the classes during the summer, when they went to a small house in the suburbs which was called Milton Cottage.

It was not until young Aleck was ten that he started to attend a private school in the city, where he remained for one year only, afterward going to the Royal High School for two years. His graduation from the high school at fourteen was normal enough but he had not distinguished himself as a scholar. This is easily understood. It takes an all-round student to stand at the head of his class but this general proficiency does not always lead, sad to relate, to an outstanding career. On the other hand, the spark of genius, which may not manifest itself in the early years and probably would be neither detected nor encouraged by teachers, limits the interest of the possessor to the one field. Only because it is demanded of him does he labor through the rest of the curriculum.

The third of the Alexanders showed early the direction in which his mind tended. He kept a museum, collecting the bones of small animals and classifying them carefully and intelligently. His interest in botany was great. He studied the stars with intensity and awe.

He had inherited a love of music from his mother and she was eager to have him develop what seemed to be a real gift. Beginning at a quite early age, he took lessons from the best music teacher in Edinburgh, a Signor Auguste Benoit Bertini. The teacher found much understanding and sensitivity in the boy and took a particular interest in him. Young Alexander enjoyed his musical tuition so much that at one stage he decided he would devote his life to music. His mother, needless to state, encouraged him eagerly in this desire. She was becoming hard of hearing (an ironic twist of circumstance that a member of the Bells should suffer in this respect) but she did not permit this to interfere with her absorption in music. She continued to play the piano with a rather pathetic insistence, even after she was not capable of hearing the notes her fingers produced. When Signor Bertini died, she gave young Aleck lessons herself and she undoubtedly was disappointed when his early ambition to be a musician receded in favor of a far more gripping purpose.

Although it seemed that everything necessary was being done to give him a proper education, the family (and young Master Aleck himself) was to receive a shock when he was sent for a year to live with his grandfather in Harrington Square. There had always been a close bond between grandfather and grandson, and the year previous the boy had displayed his feeling by writing a poem to his progenitor which began with these lines:

> I am thirteen years old, I find;
> Your birthday and mine are the same.
> I want to inherit your mind,
> As well as your much honored name.

The boy was impressed with Harrington Square. It was lined with tall houses, rather severe and dark and decidedly formidable. In the center there was a park surrounded by a high wrought-iron fence. Only the owner or tenant was allowed a key, so that the use of the park was limited to those who lived in the tall, dark houses, together with their children, their friends, their dogs, and their cats. But Harrington Square, as represented by his grandfather, was not as well impressed with the boy. Alexander had arrived in a suit of rough tweed, the coat showing some signs of wear and the trousers baggy beyond belief. The Scottish ideal of tailoring seemed to be that the durability of the cloth was more important than the success of the fitting. The old man looked him over. He was getting old, seventy-one years, and he had been living alone since the death of his second wife. The house, moreover, was large and empty, and he had been counting on having his namesake with him. But there was still in the old man a hint of the actor and dandy. After one glance he decided that something would have to be done about the boy.

So he took him to a firm of fashionable tailors and had him fitted out in proper style, even to a top hat and cane. Young Alexander's first reaction to this unaccustomed grandeur was one of dismay. He would have to wear the clothes when he returned home (for a suit, even with a growing boy, must last for more than a year) and he shuddered to think what his old friends would say of him, dressed up thus like a monkey. One is disposed to believe, however, that underneath everything he felt a secret pride in being thus arrayed like all the boys of his age who made appearances in the park below. When he went out, no doubt, he wore his glossy top hat at the proper angle and gave his cane a fine flourish. Boys, it may be added, always secretly like to be well dressed.

A second discovery followed, quite as disconcerting as the first. The boy's education had been sadly neglected. He was almost completely ignorant of Latin and Greek and did not know his way about in the classics. The outward guise of the youth had been a small matter and one easily corrected; but this was serious. "If he wants to inherit my mind," the old man said to himself, remembering the poem, "we must do something drastic about this." Certainly young Alexander must be given a better grounding in the classics as rapidly as the library at 18 Harrington Square would allow.

It was a gloomy room (All proper libraries are dark. I would think nothing of one with sunlight streaming through it and full of comfortable chairs of the modern overstuffed variety), with high french windows and somewhat funereal drapes. But the books it contained were inviting and exciting. The old man took a deep interest in his progress and introduced him to the kinds of reading which would do him the most good. To his delight the boy found that the library seemed to have everything that had been written on the allied subjects of hearing and acoustics. His interest was fired at once. He found himself, inevitably, immersed in an article entitled "Principles of the Science of Tuning Instruments with Fixed Tones." This would enchain his attention, for it dealt with certain vague ideas which he had been carrying about in his own head. Perhaps he took it to his grandfather and asked if the writer, whose name was Stanhope, had been one of the family for whom Harrington Square was named.

From what is known of the grandfather, it seems certain that such a query would result in a panegyric on the writer of the paper, that stout liberal peer (one of the most neglected great men in English history) who had been known once as Minority Stanhope because he often stood alone in the House. The Stanhope family, however, was a large one and an illustrious one, and different branches of it had held no less than three earldoms, that of Stanhope, Chesterfield, and Harrington. The authority on tuning instruments, a remarkably diversified inventor, had belonged to the Stanhope peerage.

It was, in fact, a richly useful year in every way that Alexander the Third spent with the old man, who had been forced into affluence by circumstances which had prevented him from following his own bent. Young Aleck had learned one thing he would never forget. Music could not be anything but a pleasant and genteel minor interest. The path was clear ahead. There were secrets to be learned about the manipulation of sound which nature was keeping hidden away. He must discover what they were.

He was a thorough Scot in one respect: he kept such ambitions and longings to himself. It is doubtful if his grandfather, condemned by his departure to more long years of loneliness in the dark emptiness of his fine house, was given any inkling of the strange fancies his grandson was carrying away with him.

4

The Bell family circle was complete in itself. They had friends from the outside but they did not need them. So identical were their interests that anyone outside the group of five was in a sense a stranger. Their chief pleasure was found in music. Mrs. Bell, whose power of hearing had now almost entirely deserted her, was still able to play the piano. Young Alexander was an adept at that instrument and played with the sensitive touch that Bertini had developed in him. They could all sing in the clear and resonant tones their father had taught them to employ. And the three sons could act and recite with almost the professional skill of their father.

In the field of music the family shared two enthusiasms, for Beethoven (sometimes arranged for four hands) and for Scottish ballads, the latter because of their associations. In recitation it was the Immortal Bard to whom they turned. Quotations from the musical lines of Shakespeare punctuated their conversation. If it had not been for the prejudice displayed earlier by his former church board, the father might have displayed an equal love for that laureate of the lower classes, Charles Dickens. Melville Bell's sense of humor, which all his sons shared, was alert and spontaneous. His eyes would twinkle, he would throw back his leonine head, and from his finely tuned and trained throat would issue loud, pure laughter over the slang of the coach yards and the pothouses, the anecdotes of Mark Tapley, the slyness of Sairey Gamp, and the orotund wisdom of Micawber. A familiar evening amusement was acting out scenes from Shakespeare and, one may be sure, from Dickens as well. Unable to take part because of her infirmity, their mother would sit at one side, knitting or embroidering,

34

but catching each word spoken, partly through acquaintance with the story, partly by following their lips. It is not on record that she ever complained. She had accepted her misfortune with a resignation which precluded any pettiness.

By this time Alexander the Second, the hearty, robust, and highly talented father, had completed his great work, the development of Visible Speech. He had discovered that sounds were produced by easily distinguishable physical action inside the head and throat and *that these never varied.* The roar of a lion was the result of the same use of vocal cords which produced the bark of a dog or the deep snarl of the great cats. As the action never varied, it was possible to designate them by certain symbols. The symbols, more limited in number than might be supposed, could be written down like the letters of the alphabet.

This discovery, which was to revolutionize the treatment of the deaf and dumb, was a secret at first in the Bell family circle. The father occasionally assembled an audience and then sent his sons out of the room. He would ask members of the audience to make any kind of sound which occurred to them. The response would always cover a wide range. The spectators would whisper, shout, speak fragments of Chinese, drag up from their memories a phrase from the Eskimo or even something as violent as the battle cry of the Zulu. Frequently they would imitate bird calls, blow their noses, snore, or pretend to weep.

35

Standing at the head of the room, the broadly smiling Alexander the Second would chalk on a blackboard a cabalistic device to denote each sound. Then the three sons would return to the room and proceed to imitate each sound in turn. Sometimes they would be puzzled momentarily and would whisper among themselves after studying the queer combination of symbols chalked on the board. Inevitably they unraveled the mystery, even though they might be hard put to it to produce the sound themselves. They might not be very proficient in imitating a high, weird bird call, a yawn or a snore, or the exact shading of what today is called a Bronx cheer; but they never failed to convince the audience that the symbol had conveyed to their minds the sound intended.

When the family moved to London later, the boys would occasionally assist the father in a lecture by this demonstration of Visible Speech, always to the amazement of the audience. Unknown to themselves, they were blazing the trail for the mind-reading acts on the vaudeville stage in years to follow.

Once Alexander the Third was put to a severe test. He was summoned back to the lecture room and found himself confronted with a symbol which called for the sound of the letter *t*. Fortunately he noticed a mark attached which instructed him to use a "soft palate"; in other words, he was to apply the tip of his tongue against the palate instead of touching the upper gums with it. This was quite a trick but he succeeded in doing it and the result was a curiously soft sound which resembled *k* as much as *t*, something quite foreign to the forthright English tongue.

"Bravo!" called someone in the audience. It was the man who had asked for this sound, a civil servant in India whose work was to teach Sanskrit. The sound was the Sanskrit cerebral *t*, which, of course, no one else in the room had ever heard. The rendition, declared the teacher, had been perfect.

Visible Speech was a concrete method of enabling the dumb to teach themselves how to speak. To Alexander Melville Bell it was evident that deaf mutes were silent, not because they lacked the physical organ used in speaking, but because they could not hear. Their vocal cords were ready to respond when called upon but the clamor of tongues about them meant nothing. They existed, these poor souls, lost to the finer pleasures of living, in a soundless void. But by learning the symbols they could acquire the faculty of making the sounds designated; and from this, in time, would come the ability to speak. As the organ of speech was the same in all people and the action was the same in all mouths, the symbols were universal. They meant the same to a Chinese child unable to ask for rice or a Bantu crone in an African kraal as to a deficient child in a sheltered English home.

It was a magnificent conception. Great results were obtained by all members of the family when the time came for them to teach unfortunate people in the breaking of the sound barrier.

Visible Speech became the abiding and predominant interest of all members of this highly vocal and talented family. They talked about it constantly. It was a crusade to which they were dedicating themselves. They must give their lives to teaching, to missionary work among the unfortunates who had not learned to express their wants in speech.

There had been for over a century a keen public interest in manufactured figures, called automatons, which were supposed to have human powers. This was not new, however. It had begun with the moving figures of Daedalus long before the beginning of the Christian era, and there had been iron flies and the brazen head, supposedly invented by the great Roger Bacon, which spoke words. In the middle of the eighteenth century they began to multiply. Jacques de Vaucanson constructed three figures, a flute player, a tambourine player, and a duck which quacked and flapped its wings. Finally there had been the chess players, figures resembling human beings which sat before a board and moved the chess pieces with hands encased in iron gloves. The claim was always made for them that they were so perfect they could not be beaten. At any rate, they always succeeded in soundly beating anyone who stepped up to challenge them. It was believed at the time that this was done by some form of magic, because on examination of the mechanism it seemed impossible for a man to be concealed in the works. Later it developed that a real man (who, of course, was a crack player) was able to get inside by the most ingenious of methods and from a concealed point of vantage to watch the board and move the arm of the automaton.

Flying and singing birds became more or less commonplace and these admittedly were deftly contrived by clockmakers in Switzerland. While the sons of the Bell family were growing up, there was an automaton which had been given the name of Psycho by its inventor, one J. N. Maskelyne. A new angle had been found this time, for Psycho played whist with all the skill and ferocity of a dowager.

No matter how successful they might be in some respects, the automatons had failed rather sadly when it came to the simulation of speech. It remained for a German, Baron von Kempelen, to solve this problem. The machine he introduced to the world baffled everyone by speaking; in a childish voice, it was true, but one that achieved almost natural tones. It was believed to be an imposition until the baron published a book, *The Mechanism of Human Speech*, in which he included a full explanation of the workings of the automaton.

When a duplicate of this machine was brought to the country, Melville Bell made an appointment to see it at close range. He took Alexander the Third with him.

The figure looked about as much like a human being as a doll and the sounds which came from its mouth were thin and unnatural. It was a clever imitation of the human voice, nevertheless, and young Aleck watched everything with a certain degree of amazement. His imagination took fire to such an extent that he secured a copy of the baron's book, which was written in French. He knew a little French (no more than he had been taught at high school, which was sketchy, to say the least) but somehow he grasped the sense of the inventor's explanations. This experience was an important one for him. It started his mind to thinking along lines which would lead ultimately to his great success.

After seeing the Kempelen automaton, the father decided to put his sons to a test. "My boys," he said to the two oldest, "I have a task for you. I'll give you a prize if you can make a figure which talks."

So they set to work with enthusiasm, dividing the work between them. Alexander the Third was to make the head, which meant he must fashion the mouth and tongue. His older brother was to construct the throat, complete with larynx and vocal cords. The latter started with one advantage: he was skillful in the use of tools. Alexander was somewhat thumb-fingered and found it hard to manipulate the necessary tools but he made up for this shortcoming by an ingenious decision with reference to the materials he would employ. He decided to make the head of gutta-percha, which becomes soft when subjected to heat and can be easily molded while it remains in this malleable condition. Young Alexander, moreover, might be inept with saw and plane but he had the fingers of a sculptor, long, sensitive, and capable of achieving artistic effects. Molding the soft gutta-percha in his quick fingers, he made a replica of the human skull, equipped with gums, teeth, and palate. Holes were left in the roof of the mouth for nasal passages and this necessitated the construction of a nose on the outside. Apart from the nose, he did little to achieve the semblance of a human face. In its finished condition, the skull was more on the order of a modern robot's head.

As fast as the gutta-percha cooled, the imperfections were corrected without disturbing the final form. The lips were made of iron wire covered with rubber over cotton batting. The tongue, which was to have been made of wood in connected sections and covered with rubber over cotton, proved to be so difficult and intricate that the boy never completed it to his satisfaction. He conducted many experiments with it, however, and succeeded in making a partial use of the tongue in the final operation.

The older brother in the meantime was making an artificial windpipe from a tin tube. Inside were two sheets of tin covered with rubber which could be vibrated by blowing through the windpipe.

When their father saw what they were striving to do, his face lighted up with satisfaction. Instead of attempting to copy the Kempelen figure, they had gone back to first principles and were aping nature. This, he said, was what he had hoped, for it was the only method by which the human voice could be produced with natural effects. The first test, when Alexander's minutely constructed head had been joined to Melville's ingenious throat, had to be made without a complete tongue or a proper organ bellows to pump air through the windpipe. They were too impatient to wait any longer.

The first result was sufficient to astonish them. When operated alone, the throat had produced a reedy sound. But now, when attached to the head, it gave out something unmistakably human, a deep "Ah!"

Excited beyond measure, the two boys began to experiment with ways of varying the sound. Alexander would manipulate the lips, opening and closing them, while Melville blew lustily through the windpipe. The lips began to give forth modulated sounds: *Ma-ma, Ma-ma.*

Success such as this had to be shared with the world, at any rate with the small world in which they lived. They were residing at the time in a flat at 13 South Charlotte Street, a huge stone structure with few windows and a very small entrance, which gave it some resemblance to a jail. It had been laid out with an eye to maximum living space and so one stairway served all the tenants. The stairs wound their way upward in a narrow well and there was very little light. The Bell family lived several flights up and the boys took their mechanical figure out to the dark landing. Alexander worked the lips vigorously while Melville blew into the windpipe until his face was almost purple with exertion. The gutta-percha head gave out a loud and agonizing succession of sounds.

"Mama! Mama! Mama!"

A door opened below them and an anxious voice called, "What's wrong?" Other doors opened above and below and more voices joined in the chorus of inquiry. What was wrong with the child? Had the parents left it? Where was it?

The two young inventors, satisfied with the results, picked up the robot and returned on tiptoe to their own flat, leaving the other tenants to solve the mystery of the crying child.

To Alexander the Third this had been more than an interesting experiment. He had learned exactly how human beings achieved speech. It was not simple but it was now readily understandable.

He continued with experiments of his own. The family dog, an intelligent Skye terrier, was quick at learning tricks. The boy would set him to sustained growling and at the same time would manipulate the dog's throat in order to modulate the sounds produced. Sometimes he would force his hand into the dog's mouth and close the passage at the back, which would result in an entirely different sound from the first *ma-ma-ma*. It became instead *ga-ga-ga*. After much experimenting it was possible to get a succession of sounds, such as *Ow-ah-oo gamama*. This the delighted family, and particularly the quiet Mrs. Bell, translated as "How are you, grand-mama?"

The dog was so intelligent that he began to take an interest in the tests. He would sometimes stand up on his hind legs and try to speak by himself. In fact, he became rather famous and many people came to South Charlotte Street to see and hear the talking dog.

Young Alexander Bell found in this much food for thought.

The boy had decided when quite young that the existence of three Alexanders in the family in as many generations was apt to be confusing. Having no second name, he concluded it would be proper for him to select one for himself and his fancy settled on Graham. He always said thereafter that it was because a friend of his father's, a Mr. Alexander Graham, who had returned from abroad, was visiting in Edinburgh when the Bells lived in their third home at 13 South Charlotte Street. The boy developed a liking for the visitor and he seems also to have sensed how euphonious the combination of the two names proved. He announced at the time that in future he would be Alexander Graham Bell and his parents agreed that the idea was a sound one.

It seems possible that his liking for the name went so far back that it was instinctive with him. The Grahams had been for many generations a great family in Scotland. First of all there had been that great military leader and man of noble character, James Graham, first

44

marquis of Montrose, who won so many victories for King Charles that his covenanting enemies hanged him "in his scarlet cassock in the Grassmarket." More likely still to catch the fancy of a young boy was that famous and dashing soldier, John Graham of Claverhouse, who is remembered as Bonnie Dundee. For fuller measure there were quite a number of prominent Grahams about when the boy was growing up. There was another fine soldier, General Sir Gerald Graham, who had fought with bravery through the Crimean War a few years before; also Thomas of that ilk, who was a professor of chemistry and was held in high regard in scientific circles.

Whatever the reasons, the boy became Alexander Graham Bell. He was sensitive enough to feel that his grandfather might not like it. To respect the old man's feelings in the matter, he never openly assumed the name until after the death of Alexander the First. In his later years he almost invariably referred to himself as "Graham Bell."

5

Alexander the First died in London in 1865. He makes his last appearance in a group photograph of the three Alexanders taken when his grandson was, at the most, sixteen years of age. It must be confessed that the old man dominates the picture; his hair abundant and white, his face clean-shaven, his nose and mouth firm, a thespian to the last. One is struck by the resemblance he bore to Canada's great Prime Minister, Sir Wilfrid Laurier.

In the meantime young Alexander had been engaged as a teacher of music and elocution at the Weston House Academy in Elgin and had discovered in himself a real aptitude for teaching, a liking which remained with him as long as he lived. His older brother, Melville, had stayed with their father in Edinburgh, acting as his assistant. The death of the grandfather made different arrangements necessary. Alexander Melville Bell decided to remove to London and take over his father's connections, young Alexander to follow later. The older boy remained in Edinburgh and carried on his father's classes there.

The time has come to tell something of the Bell house on Harrington Square. The square lay east of Regent's Park at the fork of Eversholt Street and Hampstead Road. It was, in reality, a triangle, the converging sides filled with tall and substantial houses, the third opening on Mornington Crescent. It lay too far north to be fashionable. To Harrington Square had drifted retired army and navy officers, widows of reasonable means, a few doctors and lawyers, some successful dabblers in the arts. Clearly it was a more pleasant place in which to live than in the rarefied atmosphere of Mayfair or the excessive affluence of Bloomsbury, where the wealthy merchants of London vied with one another in the splendor of their carriages and the gorgeous liveries of their footmen and "tigers," a tiger being a diminutive footman who stood up very straight on the step at the rear of the conveyance.

No family could be more unconventional or more blessed with lively spirits than the Bells; except, perhaps, the combination of two most aristocratic families which resulted in Harrington Square. There was, first, Anna Maria, a daughter of the third earl of Harrington, who married the Duke of Bedford. She was a lovely girl and very high-spirited herself, a niece of the eccentric fourth earl, who astonished all London by his habits. This unusual peer never made an appearance until six in the evening and then he would burst on society in the most extravagant of clothes, which he designed himself to accentuate his resemblance to that great philanderer Henri IV of France. He was odd in everything (he liked tea and had caddies in every room at Harrington House) but, when he finally married, he adopted a course which later became almost a fixed habit in the aristocracy; he chose an actress, an Irish girl, Maria Foote, who was pretty, vivacious, and universally popular, and who, moreover, introduced the song "Where Are You Going, My Pretty Maid?" The fair Maria knew exactly where she was going and she seems to have adapted herself well to life in Mayfair.

The Duke of Bedford was one of the richest peers in England. Woburn Abbey, his country seat, was a show place, filled with fine paintings and priceless furniture.

He owned great land holdings in London, including Covent Market and extensive tracts in the northern part of the city. Being resourceful in the management of his unwieldy estates, he decided to do something about his properties east of Regent's Park. It was in 1843 that he laid out the triangle which he named Harrington Square in honor of his wife. It seems to have been a real estate speculation, for none of the Harringtons lived there, preferring their London house in St. James's Place. The converging sides, with houses which loudly bespoke their respectability, were well populated when Alexander the First bought No. 18. There was still an air of morality and strict standards about the neighborhood when his son moved in to succeed him.

The house at No. 18 was all that could be expected in these days of darkest Victorianism. The ceilings were high and the windows long, necessitating the use of solidly dark hangings. There were horsehair sofas and deep chairs, and a very great deal of black mahogany, ornate round knobs, and marble slabs wherever a use could be found for one, mostly to support glass bells over curious objects of no conceivable interest to anyone. Some of the gloom was dissipated when Alexander the Second brought his family there, for this introduced laughter into the house, and animated talk and music at all times of the day. The Victorian solemnity vanished through the tall draped windows and the halls resounded with the tap of busy heels.

The family had come to London at a moment when a general upsurge of interest in scientific matters was taking place. The great impetus, perhaps, had been supplied by the publication in 1859 of Darwin's *On the Origin of Species,* an event which had rocked the world and had brought down a storm of anathema from pulpit and synod and convention. This was only one phase, however. Learned minds were turning in every direction and out of this enlightened curiosity would come, finally, the flying machine, the automobile, the motion pictures, the phonograph, in the fields of applied science.

What appealed most to the newcomers on Harrington Square was that men in all parts of the world were thinking about the problems of speech and the possibility of transmitting sound over wires and under the seas. The word "telephone" had already been coined and it crept frequently into conversations about scientific possibilities. It was not then applied to the meaning which was given it later—when the quiet youth, who sometimes accompanied the ebullient Alexander Melville Bell in his meetings with other men of scientific bent, had succeeded in creating a device which would change the whole face of life.

Chapter Three

Sunrise in
the World of Science

1

NEW horizons opened for Alexander Melville Bell
in London. Before his second son could join
him there, he had begun to meet the intellectual
giants of the day and was finding their acquaintance
exciting and stimulating. He had secured an appointment as professor of elocution at the University of London, a role which he enjoyed intensely, and had been
elected a member of the Philological Society. Among the
men he had met were Sir James Murray, who was to
become editor of the Oxford Dictionary (where he was
extraordinarily successful), Dr. Furnival, the secretary
of the society, Max Muller, a great Sanskrit scholar,
Henry Sweet, an authority on phonetics, and Alexander
John Ellis, a leader in the philological world.

Still performing his duties at Weston House Academy, young Alexander Bell was also deep in his research work. He had made a discovery, which he communicated to his father in a letter running to forty pages, a full treatise in itself. What the nineteen-year-old youth had found was that in the utterance of vowels faint musical tones could be heard back of the voice. Each vowel created a separate and distinctive accompaniment and this could be detected by holding a pencil against the cheek or throat and tapping it with a finger. This seemed to him proof that the sound of the human voice could be transmitted in other ways than by the use of the vocal cords and the tongue. In other words, he had started a train of thought, in a vague way, it is true, which proved a steppingstone to the blinding revolutionary discovery he was to make later.

The third son, Edward Charles, was with his parents and not in the best of health. Their anxiety over his condition made the parents doubly solicitous about all their sons. This was probably the reason for Alexander the Third's move from Elgin to a post at Somerset College in Bath. Being closer to London, it afforded him more frequent chances to see his parents and his delicate young brother. He seemed himself to be enjoying good health still. His energy was unflagging. He not only kept up a steady succession of classes but continued his never-ending search for the truths which still eluded his mental pursuit.

After a year at Bath, he went to London to act as his father's assistant and to complete his education at University College. This was in 1868 and he had reached his majority. At twenty-one, an age when most youths are still in the hobbledehoy stage and mostly concerned over the cut of their trousers or the fit of their jackets, this earnest young Scot was already treading hard on the heels of world fame.

The pride that his father took in him was manifested in his desire to include the boy in all contacts with the scientists of the day. He saw to it that he met Sir Charles Wheatstone and that he went to dinner at the London home of Prince Louis-Lucien Bonaparte, a nephew of the great Napoleon.

2

Sir Charles Wheatstone, well established among the recognized "greats" of the day, was already given credit for making it possible in Great Britain to transmit messages over the two-needle electric telegraph. He was, however, the most modest and retiring of men. The thought of speaking in public threw him into tremors of nervousness. Although he had been appointed professor of natural philosophy at King's College, London, he delivered no more than one brief course of lectures. They were not a success and he made no further efforts to become a teacher. Even in social contacts he was so diffident that few people ever knew him intimately.

This shy and retiring man was only happy when he was attempting to put into tangible form the curious ideas which filled his inquiring mind. The things he invented covered a wide range, and most of them were of the greatest interest to the Bells, father and son. In a room of his house he had an instrument, which resembled closely an ancient lyre, suspended on one of the walls. On occasions this instrument would begin to play music without the aid of a human hand, the strings twanging out in perfect time, sometimes ancient airs and sometimes the most modern of tunes. When the astonishment of his guests had arrived at a proper pitch, the host would explain, with a diffident smile, that it was really a most simple matter. The lyre was attached by a rod of pine wood to a piano on the floor above. The music played on the piano keyboard was transmitted over the rod by vibrations to the strings of the lyre.

It is easy to imagine the interest that young Bell took in thus seeing an open demonstration of the possibility of sending music over a simple piece of wood.

Like all shy and silent people, Wheatstone depended on external methods of amusing his guests. He would show them sand strewn over an elastic surface and then would produce a violin. The first bar of music from the violin would cause the sand to vibrate, even to twist and turn and fall into new formations.

It was inevitable that a man as curiously original as this would make discoveries in many lines. He invented the concertina, for instance, which he thought of as one of his lesser labors. He spent a great deal of time on a much more remarkable venture, which he called a polar clock. This told time by exposure to the light of the sky, even when the sun was not visible. The polar clock, however, was never more than a novelty, while the concertina brought delight to millions and has remained a popular musical instrument ever since.

Sometimes, when he had a familiar audience, he would shake off his almost morbid desire to withdraw into himself and would chat pleasantly about the ventures he was making into the world of the unknown, the strange, the inexplicable. One of his favorite subjects was the solving of cryptograms. In order to send messages beyond their borders with impunity, the governments of the world had competed in devising codes which, they believed, would keep their communications safe from the prying eyes of foreign agents. It followed inevitably that each government had also a corps of experts whose duty it was to decode the messages sent out by other countries. The British Government, no doubt, made use of Wheatstone's uncanny skill in the solving of ciphers and codes. He was never stumped. The ingenuity of the European code makers failed to evolve any system which this quiet, intent man could not unravel with apparent ease. Not content with that, Wheatstone devised a cryptogram of his own which was never deciphered!

A year after the arrival of Alexander the Second in London, Charles Wheatstone was knighted. He accepted the honor with his usual modesty, smiling faintly when acquaintances congratulated him and murmuring that it was far beyond his deserts. He had spent many sleepless nights in contemplation of the awful moment when he would have to approach and speak to Queen Victoria, and then succeed in backing out of the Presence.

3

The incident which made the most indelible impression on the mind of young Bell was a social occasion which introduced him into a new world. He and his father were invited to have dinner with Prince Louis-Lucien Bonaparte in his London home.

Something should be said first about this son of Napoleon's second brother, Lucien. Brother Lucien was the most independent of all Napoleon's kin, differing from the great man on many important points of policy and defying him to interfere in his, Lucien's, private life and his choice of wives. Lucien, known as the Prince of Canino, was married twice and had eleven children.

Louis-Lucien was born in England, in Thornygrove, Worcestershire, and grew up quite different from the rest of the Bonapartes. He had no appetite for soldiering, this stocky young man with an almost poetic cast of countenance and an air generally of the scholar about him. Instead his interests ran along scientific lines. He concerned himself with philology in particular and his greatest interests were Basque syntax and the dialects of England and Scotland. He wrote a number of books on his pet subjects. One was *The Dialects of Monmouthshire*, one had to do with Cornish literature, and his great opus was on the Basque language.

All the Bonapartes were wealthy and Louis-Lucien had inherited enough to live in high state in London. He had married many years before, when the blood ran hotter in his veins and the charms of an Italian girl named Marianne Cecchi had appealed strongly to him. There was a story current at the time that his brother Pierre shared this romantic attachment and that things reached such a pass that the two brothers had to toss a coin to decide which should have an open field. Louis-Lucien had won; although later he wondered if he would not have been luckier if he had lost.

When his cousin became French emperor with the title of Napoleon III, he went to France. He does not seem to have taken any part in politics, however. During the Second Empire, his interest still remaining fixed on the way that men yielded to environment in their speech. When the Second Empire blew up, he returned to England and continued with his investigations there.

The wife he had won with the toss of a coin was not present on the occasion of the dinner and there were only male guests. They wore, of course, the conventional evening garb of the English gentleman of the day, a long dark coat with lapels of black velvet and wide cuffs of the same material. The waistcoat opened wide to display a finely ruffled shirt, and under a high linen collar was a black tie. This fashion of dress was clearly the forerunner of the long-tailed coat of the present day but was more decorative and distinguished.

In an article written a short time before his death, Graham Bell said that the only clear recollection he still had of this occasion was of the elaborate nature of the service and the seemingly endless number of courses placed before the guests. There were, he believed, no fewer than twenty-three dishes. There would be, of course, a soup, a white fish, roast mutton, roast beef, roast ham, roast fowl, a few side dishes such as chops and kidneys and bacon, a salad, and a selection of desserts, all of French devising and rich in the extreme. It was customary to have meals as elaborate as this at the banquets and formal dinners of the Victorian era. They were hearty eaters, never having heard of calories and diets. Waistlines grew thick in the middle years. Wives and mothers, instead of remaining svelte and graceful, were decidedly plump in their thirties and of dowager-like proportions in their forties.

A footman stood behind the youth's chair and whisked away the dishes with a disconcerting suddenness. Young Aleck was so concerned with this first glimpse of life among the great that he remembered little of the conversation at table.

Memories dim as the years pass and it is easy to believe that the twenty-one-year-old Graham Bell would be likely to carry through life a clear recollection of that amazing dinner and to become hazy as to the exact things said. It can be taken for granted, however, that at the time he did not allow any of the talk to escape him, for it would be concerned with the subjects which filled his mind. The rest of his life would be spent in company where the talk would be along these lines, a continuous game of learned battledore and shuttlecock. It would be easy for him to lose the thread of the topics discussed about the abundant board of Prince Louis-Lucien. But the gargantuan meal, the costliness of the table appointments, the noiseless efficiency of the quick footmen: these, seen for the first time, he would never forget.

It has been said that George Bernard Shaw was inspired to write his great comedy *Pygmalion* by the accomplishments of the members of the Bell family. It must have been on some such occasion as this that he had the initial flash and realized what could be done with a Henry Higgins and an Eliza Doolittle. Had he been present, he would have been inspired without a doubt by the perfect modulations of Professor Bell's voice (*Bells Standard Elocutionist* was already out and selling "like hot cakes") and he would have been amused by the rather garrulous Prince Lucien, who could tell a Glasgow man from a deep-throated High-lander just as surely as Professor Henry Higgins would be able later to locate a Londoner within a few blocks of his birthplace by the distinctive atrocities he committed on the English language.

The first step that Alexander the Second took to bring his son into contact with the scientists in London was to show his long letter on resonance pitches to Alexander John Ellis. The latter had a system of his own somewhat along the lines of Visible Speech but he had been fair enough to acknowledge that Bell had gone far beyond him. He read the long epistle with the greatest interest. Although he congratulated the young man, he was compelled regretfully to inform him that a German named Helmholtz had covered the same ground years before and had published a book with the title *On the Sensations of Tone as a Psychological Basis for the Theory of Music*. The book was in German and young Bell had to base his conclusions about the Helmholtz theories by studying the plates which accompanied the text. From this he concluded that the German had discovered a method of sending vowel sounds over telegraph wires. This fired his mind as nothing else had ever done. If vowel sounds could be sent over wires, why not all sounds produced by the human tongue?

But Helmholtz, as it developed later, had not even attempted this highly imaginative step. Young Alexander had jumped to a wrong conclusion. It was well he had done so, for the conviction it planted in his mind was a factor in keeping him steadily at work on his own revolutionary ideas.

4

The word "telephone" must have come up often in the discussions that the scientists of the day, a distinguished and highly perceptive group, held among themselves. It did not mean then what it does today, however: a wonderful device by which a voice speaking at one end of a wire can be heard, clearly and instantaneously, in all parts of the world. If any of the group had used it in that guise, there would undoubtedly have been a chorus of amused reproof, "Come, come, you've been reading that absurd fellow Jules Verne."

They all read Jules Verne, of course, and it is doubtful if any of them actually considered him an absurd fellow. That industrious and highly imaginative Frenchman had a gift for peering into the future and making the stories he conceived completely believable to the general public and almost acceptable from a scientific point of view. In two years more (speaking in terms of 1870) he would reach the peak of his popularity with the publication of *Around the World in Eighty Days*. The interest of the reading public in that lively yarn would reach fever heat when a young American girl, who wrote sensational articles for the newspapers under the pen name of Nellie Bly, would set things afire by starting out alone to see if it could be done. Dressed in a shepherd's plaid coat and carrying no more than a small handbag, this intense little person with the inquisitive nose of a reporter and eyes the color of a topaz came home days ahead of the record to the thunderous applause of a watching world. Soon after this Verne would publish *Hector Servadac*, in which he would depict a man traveling in the tail of a comet, and this would prove too far-fetched even for the world-wide Verne enthusiasts and the boom would gradually die out. Nevertheless, his most successful books would continue to be read and reread and discussed, if not by the savants, at least by a general public avid for glimpses of a possible future world.

The word telephone was, in fact, almost a century old when the modern instrument which bears its name was invented. It was first used in the eighteenth century to describe a speaking tube or megaphone. At the end of that century, moreover, a German student named Huth employed it in almost its modern application in a paper on acoustic instruments.

Before the time of which we are treating, it had been used extensively by a German scientist named Philip Reis, who invented in 1860 an instrument which could transmit the pitch but not the quality of a sound. He chose the word because it derived from the Greek and meant "distant." Reis does not seem to have done anything about voice transmission but he had succeeded in constructing a machine which carried music for a distance. His device was described in a paper read before the Royal Dublin Society on November 19, 1877, as decidedly primitive. The bung of a beer barrel had been hollowed out and a core was formed in it which was covered with the skin of a German sausage. Over this was fixed a strip of platinum attached by a drop of sealing wax. This makeshift contrivance did succeed in transmitting music but the sound was always low and tinny in tone.

In the seventies the word had become almost generic and was used to describe all devices having to do with the carrying of sound over wires. Writing in 1840, Sir Charles Wheatstone had said, "When I made in 1823 my important discovery that sounds of all kinds might be transmitted perfectly and powerfully through solid wires, and reproduced in distant places, I thought I had the most efficient and economical means of establishing a telegraphic (or rather telephonic) communication between two remote points that could be thought of." The modern instrument was first called The Electric Speaking Telephone to distinguish it from all the other incomplete and nebulous devices to which the word had been applied. The general public shortened this to "telephone."

It is interesting to trace the word back to its earliest use, which was probably by a French engineer named Claude Chappe (1763–1805). He had been experimenting with the transmission of optical signals on the semaphore system and had evolved a method for sending information over a series of tall posts, erected at intervals so that each one was within range of the next in the row. Not content with this, he devoted himself to the substitution of a speaking tube or mouth trumpet for the semaphore signals. It was when he had reached this stage in his examination of communications that he employed the word telephone.

Poor Chappe suffered the fate so often reserved for those who are working far ahead of the times. His new method of sending information was neglected by the French Government and in a despondent mood he committed suicide.

Chapter Four

The Family Tragedy

1

ALEXANDER MELVILLE BELL and his wife had removed to London with a feeling that the family fortunes would be improved thereby. He had found himself almost immediately in a new world where his great gift for the teaching of proper speech and of elocution brought him wider recognition and a host of new friends. Mrs. Bell set herself to the task of making their Harrington Square home more cheerful and bright, and to pathetic efforts to escape some of the dismal consequences of her loss of hearing; watching the lips of those who addressed her and even holding an ear trumpet close to the mechanism of the piano on which her menfolk played, so she might enjoy again some of the beloved harmonies.

But underneath this outward show of cheerfulness there was a dread which left them with no mental peace. Edward Charles, their youngest son, had never been strong. The pallor of cheek and lack of weight which he took to London caused his parents much secret alarm. Could it be that the scourge of the age, the disease which settled in the lungs and claimed most of its victims from among the young, had put its mark on him?

The medical profession had failed to reach any real understanding of consumption. As fifteen years must pass before the discovery would be made that it came from the presence of bacilli in the tissues, the perplexed doctors still clung to a belief in heredity as the common cause. This had the effect of adding to the terror that phthisis (the name preferred in the profession, meaning "wasting away") inspired in the public. There was a sense of the inexorable about a disease which was handed down from generation to generation.

There does not seem to have been any hereditary tendency to the sickness on either side of the family but the despairing parents watched Edward Charles, who had just turned nineteen, with the most intense anxiety. They realized that the disease flourished in crowded cities and that even the atmosphere around Harrington Square was not conducive to any improvement. But what could be done about it?

Before they came to a full realization of the danger, the boy suddenly slumped into an advanced stage of consumption. Nothing that the best doctors of the city could suggest did anything to check the disease. Within a year of their arrival in London, he was dead.

Alexander was at the bedside when Edward died and he was deeply affected. He said little, because he realized the bravery his parents were displaying, but when he reached his own room, he took out a diary which he had been keeping. In this he set down the tragic fact in a highly poignant paragraph.

Edward died this morning at ten minutes to 4 o'clock. He was only 18 years 8 months old. He literally 'Fell asleep' He died without consciousness and without pain while he was asleep. So may I die. AGB.

2

The parents were now fully aware that something drastic must be done. The oldest boy, Melville James, was married and conducting his father's classes in Edinburgh. The reports they had of him were not reassuring and it seemed possible that he was suffering from the same disease. On one point the doctors of the day were in agreement, that consumption could be cured if caught in the early stages. The father of the boys made up his mind that he must get his two surviving sons to a more healthful and vigorous climate, even though it would mean the abandonment of the brilliant career which was opening up for him in London.

Melville Bell recalled how well he had been when he lived in Newfoundland, the mountainous island off the eastern coast of Canada where the fresh salt breezes had blown in from the sea in all directions and he had felt so vital and alive. Would the same conditions be found in Canada?

He seems to have written at once to a friend of his, the Reverend Thomas Henderson, a Baptist minister who was living in retirement in Paris, a small town in Ontario on the Grand River. Apparently he asked for advice in the matter and received every encouragement from his old acquaintance to pull up stakes and bring his family out to Canada. The question was discussed with the two surviving sons, for on November 18, 1869, the anxious father wrote a long letter to Mr. Henderson, in the course of which he said:

> I think, however—and hope that notwithstanding difficulties, we may be able to accomplish our projected trip. As for the other matter, the boys don't seem to entertain the prospect of a settlement in Canada. We must give them time to come to a decision.

But there was to be no time to come to a decision. Several months after the letter was written, the reports from Edinburgh became most alarming. The oldest son was showing the fatal symptoms, the pallor of the skin, the occasional high flush, the racking cough, the lack of energy. Young Alexander was sent at once to help him with his work, in the hope that a rest would be helpful in effecting a cure. The latter was ready to drop everything, his own classes and his experiments, to be of aid to his brother.

At first he was dismayed at the change he found. The vigor which Melville had always displayed was missing. He had become thin and pale and his high spirits had subsided into moodiness. There was little laughter in the house and the young wife confided to Alexander that she feared the worst.

"He's getting queer," she said. "He's interested in spiritualism." She hesitated to add anything more but then whispered, "He goes to séances."

This was such a change from the hearty Melville, so full of the zest of living, that Alexander began to share the wife's forebodings. For a short time only, however. Soon after his arrival, things took a turn for the better. Melville regained some, at least, of his high spirits. He began to talk of the future and all the things he planned to do. He made them laugh with imitations of Malvolio and Dogberry and Sam Weller. There was a little son in the family now who had been called Edward Charles Ottaway, after the young brother who had died and his mother's maiden name. Melville took a great interest in the child and indulged in plans for *his* future; which was of no avail, for the child died soon thereafter.

Alexander began to send reassuring reports to his parents. The doctors, he wrote, were disposed to be hopeful. The father and mother sighed with relief on the receipt of his letters. There does not seem to have been any realization in that day of a stage in the advance of the disease which seems a cruel deception on the part of nature. Just before the end there is often a definite suggestion of improvement. The patient's color seems more normal and there is a cessation in the painful coughing.

Almost without warning these favorable symptoms ceased and the final stage of the sad story was reached. Knowing, perhaps, that he had little longer to live, Melville took his wife and son to London, leaving Alexander to carry on the Edinburgh classes. The latter never saw his older brother again, for Melville died in London on May 28, 1870, at the age of twenty-five years, as suddenly as his brother two years before.

When Alexander arrived home, the distraught parents found further cause for alarm. Perhaps the strain and grief he had felt over the loss of his two brothers was responsible. Whatever the reason, it was plain to be seen that he had become unnaturally thin and pale and that he seemed to tire easily. The telltale flush could sometimes be detected in his cheeks.

The specialist who examined him gave an unfavorable report. The boy was ill, dangerously ill.

The family reached a decision at once. They would go to Canada without further delay. Melville Bell did not hesitate, although this meant giving up his rapidly growing classes, his university connections, the place he had made for himself in scientific circles. He would be starting life all over again. But nothing mattered in the face of this emergency. The boy must have a chance for his life.

3

The house on Harrington Square was sold, because it was necessary to raise a considerable sum to pay for this drastic move. No time was lost in making the necessary arrangements. A few months after Melville's death, the family took passage on a steamer for Canada. Their number had been augmented by the decision of the young widow to go with them. They arrived on August 1, 1870, within sight of the rocky dome on which the city of Quebec perches.

They continued on at once to Paris, Ontario, where the Reverend Thomas Henderson, who was to prove the most helpful of friends throughout, lived in an artistic cobblestone cottage. It was the retired minister's hope that they would settle in this pleasant town, where the quaint shops and factories of gray stone hugged the banks of the river while the residences lined the sides of the hill above. But Paris seemed too small and the Bell family felt a preference for the city of Brantford, some seven miles away. When Professor Bell was shown Tutelo Heights on the edge of that city, he knew this was the home he had sought.

And so in due course the family of four climbed one morning into a newly purchased phaeton and Melville Bell gathered the reins into his hands for the trip with which this narrative began.

All members of the family seem to have maintained an air of calm and hopefulness during these trying days, although the fact that Alexander Melville Bell had announced they were giving the new home a two-year trial was a measure of the desperation they felt. He was not certain that the move to Canada would have the desired results and yet he had thrown his career over without any hesitation to take this one chance. It seemed to those who understood the situation that he was clutching at straws.

As for the main character in the drama, Alexander Graham Bell himself, his feelings can be estimated by the references he made to the situation later in his life. "I went to Canada to die," he said on more than one occasion. He had seen his brothers die, he knew the smallness of his reserves of strength, and he was not allowing himself the comfort of too much optimism. It is possible he hoped for enough time to bring to some degree of fruition the revolutionary ideas which filled his mind.

Chapter Five

The City

1

IN those days life rolled along with little change.
Towns seemed to present the same front year after
year. Because of this I am sure I saw with my own eyes
the city of Brantford as it was when the Bell family came
to live there; for I was born a little less than nine years
after the telephone was invented. This is perhaps an
appropriate time to pause and tell something of the
background against which a truly earth-shaking event
was to take place.

Everything about Brantford seemed to be condi-
tioned by the Grand River. Originally it had been
called *O-Es-Shin-Negun-Ing*, which means "The One-
That-Washes-the-Timber-Down-and-Carries-Away-the-
Grain-and-the-Weeds." The Indians, who have a gift for
appropriate names, had not done their best in select-
ing such a prosaic label for this strong and boisterous

73

stream. The first white men to set eyes on it were Sulpician priests who traveled up and down it in canoes. They called it *La Rapide* and that was much more to the point. Finally it became known as the Grand. The name is perfect, for there is about it at most times of the year a grandeur and an unmistakable suggestion of power.

The shape of Brantford was dictated by the course of the Grand, beginning in the north, where the Ontario government had established the Institute for the Blind, a cluster of buildings with a high tower in a thickly wooded stretch of elevated land. The river here was wide and fast and had to be held in check by Wilkes' Dam a short distance below.

The river took a wide curve below Wilkes' Dam and formed a bend around a section which was not at that time put to any use; a sort of no man's land, visited only by bands of boys in search of places to swim. The beach was roughly pebbled and the land back of it was covered with weeds almost as tall as the boys who plodded through them. The river was wide here and not very deep in summertime but it narrowed and became faster of pace as it swung past an outlying section of town called Holmedale, emerging then to roll quite dangerously deep into the heart of the city. On the far side was West Brantford, the inevitable victim in the spring, when the stream became swollen and fierce. I can remember rowboats plying through West Brantford to rescue people from the roofs and top windows of their houses. Barns and chicken coops and frail outhouses for daily use would be uprooted and carried downstream. As soon as the flood was over, the philosophic residents would return to their damp and moldy homes, knowing that the same unpleasant experience would be repeated every spring thereafter.

At Tutelo Heights, the land was safe and high. It was some years after the Bell family had gone, and telephones were ringing in offices and homes all over America, that the city took matters in hand with a firm resolution and raised a protective dike on the riverbanks. It was high and wide, this dike, and it was a common boast of boys in the town that the dikes of Holland must have been poor things in comparison; for certainly the insertion of a hand, no matter how brave the owner might be, would not have done any good in the event of the Brantford dike starting to crumble.

After passing the point where Colborne Street crossed the river by way of the main bridge, the Grand took a wide, curving course of some twelve miles (Tutelo Heights being about halfway of this) and in that space dropped thirty-three feet in level. Many years before the unique Bell family took possession of the Heights, it had been decided to use the Grand as a commercial artery. But how could boats ply up and down a stream with that fatal drop? Nothing daunted, the enterprising citizens established locks near a neigh-

boring village named Cainsville, where the river regained its proper level and became calm and well behaved. All that remained then was to connect the locks
with the river at Brantford by means of a canal, and
this meant the dredging of a channel three miles long.

It proved a highly profitable venture at first. Two pas-
senger steamers named the *Red Jacket* and the *Queen*
made regular trips between Brantford and Buffalo, with
bands playing and the rails black with sight-seers. At
most times of the year wheat barges would be seen on
their way through, literally "bumper to bumper." But
times changed and the railways took over the moving of
freight. After the city had sunk hundreds of thousands
of dollars in the enterprise, the canal ceased to serve any
commercial purpose whatever. When the Bell family
crossed the Bridge on that memorable afternoon in 1870,
they could have surveyed the whole length of the despondent water route, still called by courtesy the canal,
without seeing anything break the surface except an
occasional frog, and if they had raised their noses high
enough they might have detected the faint odor which
tells of water in a stagnant state.

Five years later they shared perhaps the general
gloom when the canal and everything pertaining to it,
was sold for the handsome sum of one dollar cash down.

The city of thirteen thousand people (it has fifty thousand today) stretched along a level plateau between the
river and the high ground in the north. It was not
pretentious. There was little to attract the casual visitor

save the statue of Joseph Brant and his warriors raised in 1886. The public buildings were not particularly noteworthy. The city hall, in fact, was inadequate and, to be quite frank, unlovely. But the place had individuality. Unlike many Ontario towns where the Scottish element predominated to such a degree that at first glimpse a visitor might feel he had stepped straight into Barrie's Thrums (and a diverting impression that could be), Brantford had its own kind of charm. There was always a hint of peace and of just enough plenty about the place. The streets were all wide and the houses had sufficient ground around them to allow of high board fences on all four sides; and the fences, moreover, allowed a view of rows of hollyhocks and sweet peas and morning glories, and of back yards filled with fruit trees, healthy trees which bore unblemished apples and pears and plums. The houses were not of the gray and brown stone found so often in the aforementioned towns, but almost exclusively of white brick; sometimes faced with red and in rare cases given a touch of grandeur (or so it seemed to me) by slate roofs of several colors. For some, this created an effect of monotony, even of humbleness, but not for me. I still experience a feeling of nostalgia whenever I encounter the familiar white brick elsewhere.

There was a lamppost on every corner and a busy lamplighter, of course. The northern end of the North Ward was perhaps the final stage of the lamplighter's route. At any rate, we would see him on our way to school in the mornings and sometimes we would find him rubbing markings in chalk off the posts. These, we knew, were the cabalistic messages of tramps. There had been for twenty years or more a chronic depression in Ontario and there was a great deal of unemployment, particularly among older men. Brantford had many factories and most of them seemed able to weather the storm. Perhaps it was the smoke pouring from so many chimneys that drew the unhappy misfits. Certainly they came in great numbers, mostly oldish and beaten in spirit, grateful for any kind of "handout" and ecstatic over the gift of a dime. Looking backward I think the people of my home town were kind to them and that the messages on the posts gave the word to newcomers that here hearts were not made entirely of flint. I am happy to think this was so.

No, the individuality of the city was not achieved by scenic beauty or historic associations but could be traced to the townspeople themselves. Their cheerfulness grew out of steady employment. There was no great wealth (or at any rate it was not ostentatiously displayed) and there was little or no real poverty. Certainly there was no slum district. Those who owned carriages (a very small number) made a point of walking to church. There were as many churches in town, moreover, as there were bars, and this was a very great advance indeed. Some of the larger houses were lighted by gas but the great majority still depended on oil lamps and there was much rivalry among the housewives in finding the largest and most flamboyant shades. Perhaps I should add that coopers still made a good living by turning out round wooden bathtubs and that there was a world of opportunity in town for plumbers.

2

The men who ran the factories in Brantford must have been exceptional individuals; full of vigor and push and foresight. Although the city was one of the smallest in the country and had the most unsatisfactory and haphazard transportation facilities (the Grand Trunk had built its main line through Paris and had provided Brantford with nothing better than a spur line), it managed to keep a place among the first four or five manufacturing centers in Canada. Just about everything was made there, from fire engines to stationery.

Living so far out, the Bell family probably missed the daily occasions when the city achieved its most distinctive phase, to which I have already referred. At a quarter to seven each morning the whistles and bells would begin to sound and then the thump-thump of hurrying feet on wooden sidewalks would be heard from all directions; men starting off to work, mechanics, foremen, timekeepers, bookkeepers, owners. There were no trolley lines, and of course no motorcars or buses, so everyone walked, some carrying dinner pails. Very occasionally an executive (although the word was not used then) would be driven to work by his wife or some member of his family. I don't believe there was a coachman in the place. The factories closed at six in the evening and the sidewalks resounded again with the thump of hurrying feet.

It always seemed to me there was a grim note to the footsteps in the morning, that the men in cloth caps or well-worn fedoras were reluctant to take up again the labors of existence. But in the evenings it was different. There was a briskness, even a hint of jauntiness, in the thump of heels. They called back and forth to one another as they made their way homeward.

But they had put in ten hours of steady work! One concession only was made. The quitting whistles blew on Saturdays at five o'clock. By reason of this early closing, the younger men could be home and washed up and togged out in their best in time for the great occasion of the whole week, the Saturday evening parade on Colborne Street.

The parade was not exactly a gay affair. In fact, it always seemed rather solemn and tiring. Back and forth they went, on three commercial blocks on the north side of the street, the men and the girls keeping separate lines for the most part. There was a restraint about it, a rather complete sobriety. It was, however, the matrimonial mart, the place and the time where boy met girl. It was no wonder that a song was very popular which went something like this:

If every night was Saturday night,
And every day was Sunday!

It was due to the hard times which kept a grip on the whole country that labor conditions remained static through all these years. Certainly wages showed no tendency to climb. Ten dollars a week was good, solid pay. Men who made as much as a thousand dollars a year were substantial citizens. If they made more than that, they could afford to keep a horse and buggy and have one of those houses with red brick facings and slate roofs.

The Bell family had always lived in an academic and cultural atmosphere and so this was like a new world to them. That they had not held themselves aloof was evident when Graham Bell returned to the city on a visit many years after. The main line of the railway had been built through Brantford in the meantime and he commented on this enthusiastically. "Ah, those splendid factories," he said. "How good it must be for them!"

3

The city was still so close to the Bell era when I was a boy that much of the adult talk I heard bore on the great event. Businessmen and storekeepers, who had telephones, were inclined to boast of it. When the tracks were being laid for the electric trolley lines and my mother took my brother Bill and me over to Brant Avenue to inspect them and to receive her warning that we must never step on the ground rails (all mothers were disturbed about them), there was a general disposition to link this up with the telephone. "My, did Mr. Bell invent this too?" people asked, and the query carried the implication that, if he had, everything would be safe and proper.

I keep casting back into my memory for anything that had a direct connection with the Bell family. There was Dr. Kelly, for instance, who had been inspector of public schools when they lived at Tutelo Heights and had been on friendly terms with them. He was still inspector when I was enrolled at the North Ward School, a rather dismal building with a wooden platform in front and a winding stairs inside which made the place a first-grade firetrap. I remember his first visit of inspection very clearly. He came in quietly and seated himself near the teacher's desk, a stout old man with a square face and a mop of unruly gray hair. We were all properly subdued, fearing we would be lined up and put through some trying tests.

Instead the amiable doctor began to talk to us about poets. I had only the vaguest idea what a poet was but my interest was caught at once. He told us of the first piece of verse that Byron wrote. It made so great an impression on me that I have never been able to forget it. This was how it went:

> There was an old lady in Gretna Green;
> The meanest old lady that ever was seen.
> And when she dies, which I hope will be soon,
> She firmly believes she will go to the moon.

The next time the good doctor visited us, he settled down with a smile. "Today," he said, "I am going to tell you some stories about a great man who lived here not so long ago. His name was Alexander Graham Bell."

It is humiliating that one can retain in the mind matters of no importance whatever and completely forget things of great interest. I have remembered that bit of Byronic doggerel but of what the inspector told us about Tutelo Heights and the invention of the telephone, I recall not a word!

Graham Bell voted once only in his life and that was in Brantford. We took our politics very seriously there and had become known as the City of the Three Thunders, because a trio of leaders were called Great Thunder, Big Thunder, and Little Thunder. All three were very much in the public eye but, as they were Liberals, we put small stock in them at home, my father being what was called a "dyed-in-the-wool Tory." When Graham Bell came of age, William Patterson (Big Thunder) announced himself a candidate for mayor and the young Scot cast his vote for him. After leaving Brantford, Mr. Bell moved to Washington, D.C., where permanent residents did not have the franchise. As a result he never had a chance thereafter to cast another vote.

That he voted for a Liberal did not mean he agreed with the political philosophy of that party. The distinction between the two parties in Canada was not closely drawn but I wish it had been known on which side of the fence he stood. It would serve as a lead to certain phases of his character which do not seem to have been explored. It is quite possible that he did not take politics seriously then, for at Tutelo Heights the talk was always of music, of the stage, of improving the sad lot of the deaf and dumb, and of the advances in science. There was little concern about the struggles of the Ins and Outs.

Nevertheless, I wish I had raised the point when I had the privilege of interviewing him. This was in 1906, when the city invited him back for a banquet in his honor. I was a reporter on the *Expositor* and I hurried out to see him as soon as he arrived. He answered all my questions but I was very young at the time and I am afraid they were quite cut and dried. Ah, if there were only something in the theory of the transposition of epochs and that time could be changed backward and forward. I might have that talk with him today instead of more than fifty years ago. There are countless questions I would like to ask him now.

4

The original grant to Joseph Brant was a strip of six miles along each side of the Grand River, which included all of the land about Tutelo Heights. The winding road there today was originally an Indian trail. The man Stewart owned a thousand acres, which came to

him with his Indian bride and he used to ride out in a
fine carriage behind well-groomed horses and with
a coachman. This, however, was long before the Bells
arrived. The new occupants of the Heights made many
friends among the descendants of the Six Nations.

The young inventor was very much interested in the
language of the Mohawks. He studied it with care and
used it on many occasions, once on the telephone. This
so pleased them that he was made a member of the tribe
with all the usual ceremonial. The steps of the war
dance and the colorful costume with its headdress as
gorgeous as a peacock's appealed to his sense of the
theatrical. When any occasion arose for a celebration,
he would get into his new costume with its fringe and
beads and plumes.

Somewhere in the early years of the nineteenth century there lived on the Six Nations Reserve a noted
orator whose name was Chief John (Smoke) Johnson.
The Indian race has always been noted for the gift of
oratory and the Six Nations seem to have excelled all
others in that respect as in so many other ways. Readers
of Canadian history will recall that the Iroquois (the
tribal name of the Six Nations), who fought so furiously
against the French settlers, invariably had a leader who
could charm everyone within sound of his voice, even
the hated Frenchmen. In those distant days they were
inclined to apply nicknames to their spokesmen, sometimes affectionate, sometimes amusing, but there was
nothing save deepest respect in the name they had

coined for Chief Smoke Johnson, who was called the Mohawk Warbler.

It happened that a charming English girl, Emily Howells (who bore some relationship to the American novelist William Dean Howells), came to live with her sister, who had married a clergyman named Elliott. The latter was engaged in missionary work on the Six Nations Reserve and one of the first pupils who came to him for an education was a son of the Mohawk Warbler, Chief G. H. M. Johnson. A description of him has come down on the records, "tall, reserved, with the great dark eyes and handsome nose of his race." The young couple fell in love and they were married in due course. He was a man of substance apparently, for he took his bride to a home of considerable dimensions, which they called Chiefswood.

About twelve miles south of Brantford on a pleasant site facing the river there is still a sign on the road which reads *This is Chiefswood.* The large house is said to have been copied from a baronial home seen by the young chief in England. The front and back are identical, one door facing the road and the other looking out over the river. Here a family of four children was raised in a high degree of pomp. One writer has left a description in which emphasis is laid on the dining room, where a long table was spread with glistening silver and glass. The rooms were large and of imposing proportions. Chiefswood became, in fact, the show place of the proud people who had followed Joseph Brant into exile.

Here was born in the year 1862 the last of the four children, a girl who was destined to become the great Indian poetess, E. Pauline Johnson. The Bell family paid a visit to Chiefswood and were much impressed with the beauty of the setting, and even more particularly with the charm of the young daughter, with her dark and expressive eyes, her finely modeled features, and her voice, which was rich and warm and capable of expressing every emotion. She had done nothing to distinguish herself at that time but within two years after the visit she astonished a small circle of friends by writing in an album some impromptu lines which began:

> Pine trees sobbing a weird unrest,
>   In saddened strains,
> Crows flying slowly into the west
>   As daylight wanes;
> Breezes that die in a stifled breath,
>   O, Happy breezes, embraced by death.

It was not until 1892 that she appeared on a platform for the first time and displayed the gifts which, combined with her dark beauty, made her a platform favorite for the balance of her life. It is to be regretted that the Bells, father and son, who were so dedicated to the proper production of the voice, had no opportunity of hearing her recite.

Chapter Six

Family Life
at Tutelo Heights

1

THE Brantford newspapers in 1870 were chatty and informative on certain matters, such as local politics. The advertisements called to the attention of readers such things as Irving's Canadian Series, five-cent music, matrimonial feelers (only genuine answers noticed), Daniel Clifford, undertaker, with the best hearse in any town or city in the West, Campbell's Quinine Wine (public warned against imitations), real estate chances (small house wanted not to cost more than five hundred dollars), and many others of like nature. But nowhere, either in the news or the advertisements, was there any hint that the city had special advantages as a health resort.

This must have been an oversight. Or was the case of

Alexander Bell the one shining example of what this city on the Grand River had to offer in the way of health-giving atmosphere and invigorating breezes? He arrived at Tutelo Heights in August 1870 and, as has been remarked, he looked a little "peaked." His father and mother watched him and took every precaution to prevent any overexertion on his part. It is likely that he did some light work around the house and on the grounds but the greatest part of his time was spent on the edge of the Heights, where the line of tall birch trees guarded against the sharp descent to the river. There was enough space between two of them to swing a hammock. Here he would lie and watch the river rolling along below and let his gaze rest lazily on the chimneys and spires of the city to the north. He seems to have shown an improvement almost from the start.

Before the summer was out he was doing whatever was required on the grounds, cutting the grass, grooming the horse, washing the phaeton. During the winter he continued to attend to the horse and did whatever was needed in the way of shoveling snow; and that was quite a chore, considering the distance between the house and the road. He went on sleigh rides with the other young people of the neighborhood, wrapped up warmly in buffalo skins and blankets, for the winters in Brantford were cold and it seemed sometimes to the un-initiated arrivals from warmer climes that a wind blew straight down the Grand River from the North Pole with the Heights as its special target.

By the time spring came he was a new man. He had filled out some and the color in his cheeks was nature's hallmark of good health and not an indication of germs burrowing within him. The two-year chance had worked. His parents said to themselves that God and the air of Brantford had been good and had brought recovery to their sole surviving son.

Alexander Melville Bell had gone to Boston in the autumn of 1870 to fulfill his lecture engagements there and had been so successful that there was immediate discussion of a return engagement. His theories on Visible Speech had attracted wide attention and he was asked to lecture on that subject later. This he was compelled to decline because of arrangements already made in Canada, but consideration was promised to his suggestion that his son take his place.

The son was eager for the chance. Teaching was in his blood. He had come to enjoy it, to feel that it could be made his life work, if the theories at the back of his mind came to nought. The leisure he had enjoyed since their arrival at Tutelo Heights had been welcome at first but now, with the evidence of improved health apparent in the new vigor he felt, he was anxious to get back into harness. It was a matter of jubilation, therefore, when he was notified early in 1871 that the Boston School Board had voted five hundred dollars as remuneration for lectures he was to deliver at the Boston School for the Deaf and at the Clarke Institute for

Deaf-mutes in Northampton. He left in April of that year to begin his duties.

During the eight months he had spent with his parents at Tutelo Heights he had not been idle. Swinging in his hammock between the two birch trees, he had kept his mind continuously on his problems. In the workroom, which lay in the angle of the drawing room and the conservatory, he had gone back to studying tuning forks. At the piano he was more likely to experiment with single tones than to play music. For long stretches of time he would sit and ponder and listen and his parents would say to one another, "Aleck is at it again." His father understood what his son was trying to do and was fully in sympathy with it, because he had evolved the symbols which made up Visible Speech by the same methods. This, however, was different. Electricity played a great part in it and Mr. Bell Sr., did not have much understanding of the laws governing that amazing mystery of nature. He took his son's work seriously, even though he was prone at times to make fun of it.

It is important to bear in mind that what Graham Bell was striving to accomplish at this time was an improvement on the telegraph. The telephone was something for the future, a great objective which would never come to anything unless he discovered a new scientific approach. On the other hand, he had a definite idea for an improvement in the telegraph, which was being em-

ployed all over the civilized world but was still limited
to the sending of one message over a wire at one time.
The Bell plan was to make use of the law of sympathetic
vibration and send any number of messages in the
Morse code on a single wire. This, he was convinced,
could be done without any interference or confusion.
He called it "harmonic" or "multiple" telegraph. This
was something, needless to state, that many others
were striving to achieve.

Graham Bell completed his device within the
next two years and was granted a patent. It was never
taken over by the telegraph companies, perhaps because
they thought it had a flaw which made practical use
difficult.

But out of the work he was doing on the harmonic
telegraph came a hint, a flash, and finally a blinding
light.

2

The Bell family gained a quick popularity in Brantford. People who met them were charmed with the new
arrivals, particularly those who were fortunate enough
to be invited for an evening at Tutelo Heights. There
was a lack of formality, a gaiety, about a reception
there. There was music always, the best of music. There
was the head of the family, his darkly luminous eyes
lighting up his bearded face, always to be depended on
for inimitable and spirited recitations. There were com-

petitive games on the order of charades. Father and son were equally involved in these social activities. Mrs. Bell's hearing was growing progressively worse and her part was generally that of an onlooker.

Sometimes the parties were quite large, as many as a score of people taking to their buggies or sleighs, according to the season, and driving up the long, winding road to the Heights. After the full significance of what young Aleck had accomplished burst upon the world and in particular upon a proud and properly boastful Brantford, it became a habit for people to tell, in the form of articles and letters, of the occasions they had spent with the Bells in their quaint home. Some of these accounts are still available.

It is probable that the family was rather hard-pressed for funds during the first two or three years. Melville Bell had the income from his lectures, of course, and there must have been royalties coming in from *Bells Standard Elocutionist*. But the property was not easy to maintain and traveling expenses would constitute a drain on the family purse. This must have been the reason for the concerts given at intervals, sometimes in other cities, sometimes in Brantford. When the home town was thus honored, it was generally in Wycliffe Hall, which could accommodate large audiences. Melville Bell was the star performer on these occasions and his vibrant readings from Shakespeare created a new interest in the Bard. The newspaper reports gave no indication of what the talented family gained (at twenty-five cents a head)

94

from these efforts to entertain. Unfortunately people did not line up with blankets and mattresses and wait through wintry nights to buy tickets when the box office opened as they did when Charles Dickens gave his readings in New York; nor could Brantford equal the eight thousand pounds' profit that Boston yielded Dickens for a week of appearances. If they had, it is quite possible that the telephone would never have been invented.

It became customary to call on the members of the Bell family when any public celebration was to be held. Consider this report, for instance, from the Brantford *Courier* of August 19, 1871:

The day [the centenary anniversary of Sir Walter Scott] was celebrated here in the most befitting manner, the programme being confined to the reproduction of some of the great author's own creations. Prof. Melville Bell's great elocutionary powers were brought into requisition, and all who heard his reading will bear us out in the assertion that he literally caused many of the *dramatis personae* of Scott's works to pass in review before the admiring eyes of his audience. The beautiful and pathetic poem *The Lady of the Lake* was first read and, as was remarked, even those who had never seen the sublime scenery depicted could almost feel themselves in the presence of those towering rocks and crags and hear the splash of the oars in the waters of Loch Katrine.

The local scribe, it seems, had been much impressed.

Melville Bell's brother, David Charles, came out from Dublin to join the family in 1874, securing a comfortable brick residence on Palace Street (still standing, of course, for Brantford seldom tears a house down) and taking thereafter an active part in all entertainments.

Before long, elocution became a favorite subject in the schools, where it had been rather neglected before. The *Expositor* of June 11, 1875, tells of pupils in Langford, a small village, giving *Casabianca* and *Hohen linden* with a verve which delighted their parents at least. *Casabianca* must have been in the school readers of that day, because I can remember my fellow students stumbling through its melodramatic verses and one tragic occasion when I was summoned to the platform to do the same.

Young Aleck Bell was well liked but he did not start hearts to fluttering among the young ladies of the town. Perhaps he was more interested in the defective ears and vocal cords of his pupils and not enough in the bright eyes of his partners. He made many friends among the young men. His relationship with a man of his own age named George Dempster must have been on a Damon-and-Pythias footing. George had evening clothes while Graham didn't. When they were invited to the same parties, they would take turns, one wearing the clothes while the other stayed home.

People of all ages found, however, that this

young man, with his still pale cheeks framed in the scantiest of black whiskers, repaid a closer acquaintance. There was a rather memorable occasion when the Governor General of Canada, the earl of Dufferin, came to the city on August 25, 1874, to turn the sod for the Brantford, Norfolk and Port Burwell Railway. A dinner was given for the earl and countess at Bow Park, the summer residence of the Honorable George E. Brown, at one time premier and the owner of the Toronto *Globe*. Alexander Graham Bell was one of the least important guests and when young Mrs. G. H. Wilkes found she had drawn him as a partner, she did not anticipate a stimulating evening. But almost from the start she discovered that this young man, although he seemed almost obsessed with strange subjects, had a way of making them seem fascinating. The experiments on which he was engaged, and of which she had heard curious reports, became engrossing when he proceeded to tell her about them. His eyes lighted up and he chose his words with singular perception. The young matron was interested to the extent of regretting that the dinner had to end in time for the guests to attend a civic reception in the city hall at eight-thirty.

3

No story of the Bell family in their Brantford home is more illuminating than that of the coming of William Sloane.

The latter was born in England with many physical disabilities. Stone deaf, with weak eyesight and defective speech, he was a farm drudge with an uncle in Yorkshire. The little money he was able to put together was just enough to bring him out to Canada at the age of nineteen. He arrived with empty pockets in the dead of winter and encountered great hardships in his search for work. Kicked about from one farm to another, he was finally taken in by an elderly English woman and given a bed for the night. This must have been in the neighborhood of Brantford, for in the morning she gave him a slip of paper with a name and address on it.

"They are kind people," she said. "Perhaps they can do something for you."

The name on the paper was that of Alexander Melville Bell of Tutelo Heights.

It had been snowing heavily during the night but now the storm was over and a cold wind was sweeping in from the west. The poor drudge, lacking an overcoat, struggled along the drifted roads until a sleigh, containing two men, overtook him. They pulled up.

"Where are you going?" asked the older of the two.

Unable to hear, and so numbed with the cold that his small capacity for speech had deserted him, the unfortunate man held up the slip of paper by way of answer.

The bearded older man looked at it and then drew out a pencil from under his heavy overcoat. "Where are you from?" he wrote on the paper.

Sloane took the slip and managed to set down the word "England."

The two occupants of the sleigh looked at one another questioningly and then each nodded. The older man motioned to the shivering wayfarer to climb into the back seat and wrap himself up in a rug. By the most fortunate of coincidences, the wanderer had encountered the two Bells.

Unable to speak and not convinced of his good fortune, he beseeched them with silent eyes for the help he needed, while the wind cut across the hardening surface of the snow and carried with it a white spume which lodged in every crease of his thin clothes.

Melville Bell repeated the gesture. "Get in, get in," he said.

A very kind lady, carrying a large ear trumpet, took him in hand after they arrived home. He was given a substantial warm meal and then shown to a bed, where he slept soundly the rest of the day.

It was Mrs. Bell who conveyed the welcome news to the wanderer later that they would make a place for him if he wanted to stay. She handed him a note. "My son wants you to stay here with us. He is teaching the deaf to talk in Boston. He will teach you to talk. You can bring in the wood, go for the mail, and do other jobs around the place, and we will pay you seventy-five dollars a year."

The grateful man remained with the family for several years. When Graham was home on his frequent vacations, he set himself seriously to the task of teaching Sloane to talk. The latter learned to read lips and to form words by use of Visible Speech. The hardest test came when the young teacher decided Sloane must learn to say "Massachusetts." The pupil struggled with that most difficult of words for the three weeks of Graham's visit and did not seem to be making much headway.

"Try! Try!" protested the teacher. "Keep on trying. Never give up."

The day before Graham Bell was due to return to Boston, Sloane came to him with a look of satisfaction on his face. In slow and halting tones, he said the word "Mass-ses-tu-sets."

There was jubilation in the household over this triumph and the handicapped man made quicker progress from that time on. He finally reached the stage where he could carry on conversations with the members of the family.

He was still with them in 1876, the decisive year, and played a part in those exciting days, which will be referred to in due course. When he left Tutelo Heights a short time after the Great Event, he could speak well enough to find employment in the Middle West, selling soap from door to door. Graham Bell continued to write letters to "Dear William" as long as he lived and generally enclosed a check in the fear that the demand for soap had been slow.

It was the father of the family, Alexander the Second,

who established the tone of the household. He seemed always to be in exuberant mood and took it on himself to keep guests amused.

Once he was driving along a road in the neighborhood of the Heights and was stopped by some young people who wanted directions to the Bell house. He did not know them but, without revealing his identity, he gave careful instructions as to the way, and then drove on. When they arrived, he himself opened the door, garbed in an oriental robe and holding a long-stemmed pipe in one hand. Bowing with eastern profusion, he invited them in and told them to make themselves at home.

He became so well liked that when he decided to move his family to Washington in 1881, to rejoin his son, who had married and settled himself in the American capital, he was given a complimentary banquet by the citizens of Brantford. The speeches delivered on that occasion show how deep a hold he had attained on their affections.

No measures were taken to keep secret the nature of the experiments being carried on at Tutelo Heights. Melville Bell would wink at acquaintances and say, "Aleck? He's out in the barn and thinks he can talk over wires and tin cans," but he was always willing to explain seriously the nature of the research on which his son was engaged.

They had made the acquaintance of a resident of the city named Mason, who owned a property at the corner of Colborne and King streets. He must have conducted a store at that location but the nature of his business has not been ascertained. Graham Bell would come in frequently to play chess with Mr. Mason and for convenience's sake had put up a wire between the store and a house several blocks away. The other members of the Bell family would go to this house and, when ready to start for home, would "buzz" a signal over the wire to warn Graham to finish the game and be ready to start.

Stories circulated all over town about what the son of the family was striving to do. The general consensus seemed to be "It's ingenious but it will never be anything but a toy." Melville Bell heard that opinion expressed many times when he was striving to finance the work. Even after the success of the final test, the moneyed men of Brantford kept their wallets out of sight and shook their heads in doubt. It was still a toy to them.

A digression may be in order at this point. After the telephone became a commercial possibility, the inventor gave his father an interest of 75 per cent in the Canadian rights. The other 25 per cent went to Charles Williams, Jr., of Boston, in return for which he was to supply Professor Bell with one thousand telephones free of charge. This arrangement did not prove very satisfactory. The Canadian Government stepped in and charged a duty on the telephones. This, together with other unexpected expenses, raised the costs to an almost prohibitive level.

4

The young widow of Melville James, the oldest son, who had come out to Canada with the family, was a charming girl and made many friends quickly in the city. She found a second husband in the person of a young farmer named George Ballachey. In 1875 a son was born, who was named after his father. The young couple lived on what was known as the back road to Mount Pleasant and had the honor later of installing the first rural telephone. It was placed in a window of the dining room and many times a day carriages would stop on the road outside and people would stare at the curious machine.

The boy's first recollection of Tutelo Heights was of an occasion when his mother took him there. He could not have been more than two years old at the time but he recalls being led up a long walk to the house between hedges which seemed very high to him. Apparently he was allowed to go out into the back garden by himself but he did not wander far away. His attention had been won immediately by something quite strange. There was a wire attached to the roof of the room behind the glass house where the flowers grew. It stretched out across the garden and disappeared into the roof of a building behind the house. This, when he became older, he identified as the barn.

Apparently he was an observant child, for he gave

this his full attention. He had never before seen a house with a wire like that. What was it for? He was still looking up at it when Alexander Melville Bell came up the path through the orchard. The latter stopped beside the boy and his eyes twinkled when he saw how absorbed the little fellow was.

A talk ensued between them. Unfortunately the mind of a boy of two is not capable of retaining any recollection of things that grown-ups say to them. All that George Ballachey, who is still living in Brantford, remembers of this occasion is that his "uncle" Melville seemed very much in earnest. The personality of Melville Bell has been stamped indelibly on the record of those days and so it is not difficult to draw some conclusions as to what he might have said. Possibly it went something like this:

"I see you are wondering about that wire, my boy. Lots of people, grown-ups all of them, have been wondering about it. And now they are beginning to wonder and to talk about it all over the world. Yes, my boy, you must always remember this if you can, for what you are looking at is the first wire of the kind that has ever been seen. Some day"—there would perhaps be a gesture of the eloquent hand at this point—"there will be wires like this running in and out of all the houses in the world. It was your own uncle Aleck who knew how to make it. You will understand all about it some day."

During the first years of his life little George

Ballachey was often at Tutelo Heights but he has few, if any, memories of his uncle Aleck, who was away most of the time and very busy about this matter of wires and getting married. It was Great-uncle Melville he remembers best, the kindly man with the long black beard and the strong, clear voice. They became the best of friends. The first thing the boy would do when he was taken to the house was to hurry out into the long back garden in search of his uncle. He knew where to go, for his uncle Melville made much use of the space between the birch trees overlooking the river. He recalls now that Melville Bell took a great deal of interest in the way he spoke.

"Come, little fellow, that's not how to talk," he would say. "Now listen to me."

The boy would look and listen and, as he grew older, he would seriously attempt to speak in the proper way. The result was that he learned to express himself properly and distinctly.

It is one of his chief regrets that he did not arrive on the scene early enough to have a clear memory of what was going on in the house in the long garden, where wires sprouted out mysteriously from unexpected places and an air of suppressed excitement seemed always to prevail. It would have been wonderful to participate in the days when all the difficulties were triumphantly cleared away, the time of the coming of the sudden prosperity.

5

Alexander the Second remained, throughout the years which followed, a very close friend of the Reverend Thomas Henderson. After the telephone was invented, this worthy pair, the teacher of elocution and the retired minister, who had little business sense between them and even less commercial experience, took on the management of a telephone company in Canada. They had to knock into heads as hard as the rocks which covered so many of the farms of the day that a myth had become a reality, that what had been considered a toy was something that would revolutionize all of life.

Somehow they did it, these two oldish men, the professor with his great mane of white hair and his whiskers as profuse as the beard of Abraham, and the retired "meenister," whose hair had turned a fine gray and was worn long and brushed severely back. They induced people to set up telephone lines between houses or between a residence and an office. When sweeping improvements a few years later made "central" offices possible, so that all subscribers in a town could talk back and forth among themselves, these two charmingly uninitiated babes in the wood took that matter in hand also. The first central plant in Canada was installed in 1878 in the city of Hamilton, which lay about twenty-five miles east of Brantford, and very soon after, a half dozen other towns had also been equipped. The advertisements the pair used were as quaint as an old lady's silver "stomacher" but the admissions and doubts they expressed in the "copy" proved more effective than bombastic claims. Their business letters would have evoked squawks of protest from a modern office manager. But somehow they kept things on an even keel and the company prospered.

But at this early stage of the telephone story, our concern is with the life that was lived at Tutelo Heights. In the company of friends Alexander Melville Bell would often show his skill with tricks of magic. He was as swift and sure with his hands as a stage practitioner of legerdemain.

The two old friends visited back and forth during the early seventies and sometimes they would take advantage of the chance to call on an acquaintance of Mr. Henderson's who lived on the Paris Road, a short distance from Paris itself, Mr. William Moyle, a gentleman farmer. Melville Bell gave a number of profitable programs in that town and it became a habit for them to drop off at the Moyle house for a late breakfast on the way back to Tutelo Heights the next morning. Dr. James H. Moyle, a grandson, who is a practicing dentist in Brantford today, heard from his father and an older brother a great deal about these friendly calls. The entertainments were generally given during the winter season and so the breakfast guests would arrive in a sleigh with a loud jingling of bells and much cheerful calling of greetings. Breakfast would be a leisurely meal.

Grandfather Moyle, unfortunately, for all concerned, was one of the tough-grained investors to whom Bell participation was offered in vain. His two old friends were so anxious to have him participate that they offered him shares at twenty-five cents. It seems, however, that he knew his own mind well enough not to hesitate. His answer was "No."

One of the legends which has come down in the Moyle family is that in the relaxing period which follows a satisfactory meal, Melville Bell would explain exactly how he performed his magic tricks. He employed, among others, the ancient but always sure-fire trick of borrowing a hat from someone in the company, making sure to get a "plug" hat (the popular name at the time for one of the high silk varieties) and then breaking eggs into it. This he explained while breaking some eggs apparently into the best hat of his nervous host.

The wide knowledge and understanding of Alexander Melville Bell was a legend which has come down through the better part of a century in the Moyle family, hand in hand with stories of the quiet and intense son, Alexander Graham Bell. Although the head of the family said "Nonsense!" when he was told that Aleck had at last received messages in Paris over a telegraph wire from his father and friends in Brantford, there was a thorough appreciation in the Moyle clan of the latent power in the Bell son.

Anna Moyle, a niece of William Moyle, was visiting with the Bells (she seems to have been some years younger than Graham Bell) and the son of the family, having occasion to drive into Brantford, invited her to go with him. As they were leaving, Professor Bell came hurrying out from the house with several letters. He looked hard at his son when placing them in his hands.

"Aleck," he said, "we can just make the English mail with these. Be sure and post them. They're very important."

The drive into town was a pleasant one. It was winter and the roads were packed with snow. The pleasure of the outing for Aleck Bell was enhanced when he saw, while driving through West Brantford, two small girls talking in the finger language of the deaf and dumb. He pulled on the reins and was out of the sleigh before it could be brought to a complete stop. He not only talked to the two children, using his fingers, but he went inside their home to see their mother in order to discuss with her the training of the girls. This took quite a time but he came out feeling that it had been well spent. When they reached the post office in town, he left Anna in the sleigh and took the letters in to mail. In a few minutes he came out with his hands full of correspondence, mostly from the Old Country.

When they reached home, Melville Bell was at the door with an immediate question.

"Did you mail my letters, Aleck?"

A blank look came over the son's face. He touched the pocket of his overcoat with a gesture of regret.

"I'm sorry," he said. "I forgot all about them."

For once the bearded countenance of Alexander the Second showed signs of chagrin and annoyance. "Then they've missed the English mail!" he exclaimed. "Aleck, Aleck, what's in your head? You'll never be worth a row of pins."

Chapter Seven

A Tale of Two Cities

1

DURING the five years which followed his first trip to Boston, Alexander Graham Bell lived a life of intense activity and concentration. Most of his time was spent in Boston, lecturing at the Horace Mann School, conducting private classes of his own, and at all times going on with his experiments. As soon as the school closed, he would return to Brantford, to catch up on sleep, to have regular meals again, and to lie out in the sun on the edge of the high bluff over the Grand; and, of course, to continue his ceaseless search for the secrets which evaded him. The air at Tutelo Heights might be just plain, everyday ozone to the natives but it was renewed health and quick recuperation to the last of the Bell sons.

He was one of those rare young men who feel that home ties are of the first importance. Melville Bell heard everything that his son was doing. When the youth returned to Brantford for his long visits, he was full of detailed reports on the progress he was making with his experiments as well as of the people who figured in his Boston life. While away he wrote long letters to his father, some of the most important of which have, fortunately, been preserved, many of them having a bearing on his gradual advance to the great solution.

They heard, for instance, about his good fortune in being thrown into contact with two friendly and fair-minded men, both of whom were citizens of considerable means and who would in time take over the financing of his scientific endeavors. This came about because each of them had a child whose hearing was impaired and who grasped eagerly at any opportunity to speak properly in spite of this handicap. The first of these kindly backers was Thomas Sanders of Haverhill, whose son George had been born deaf. The boy was five years old when his training was placed in the hands of Graham Bell. Thomas Sanders was so solicitous about his little son that he arranged for the boy and a nurse to live at the boardinghouse where Bell lodged. This was done, of course, so that the teacher would have the opportunity to keep little George under constant observation and care. A year later a better arrangement was made. The boy's grandmother lived in a roomy colonial house in Salem and the boy and his nurse were sent there for the winters, Bell being invited also to make his home with them. The distance between Boston and Salem was only fourteen miles and would not prevent him from getting into the city for his classes. The white clapboard house, moreover, was much more comfortable than any boardinghouse which he could afford and so this solution was a happy one. Old Mrs. Sanders was both gracious and helpful, even to the extent of offering the young inventor the whole of the basement for his experiments. Later, when the basement seemed to be getting overcrowded with coils of wire, curious kinds of apparatus which he identified to his hostess as batteries, packing boxes of this and cases of that, Mrs. Sanders decided to give him the use of the attic as well. Here it was lighter, roomier, and more pleasant generally but he continued to make some use of the basement, largely because he wanted to string wires between the two. If Mrs. Sanders was taken aback, she was too kind to say anything.

In the meantime he was getting along well in teaching little George how to speak. The boy took a great liking to his mentor and would follow him everywhere in the house, sitting on boxes or using coils of wire for the purpose, watching with wide-open eyes. Occasionally he would ask a question in slow and labored tones.

The other sponsor was a Boston lawyer and industrialist named Gardiner Greene Hubbard, a grandson of the Gardiner Greene who had been in his day the financial plutocrat of Boston. He went to Graham Bell as soon as the latter began to acquire a reputation and talked to him about one of his daughters, Mabel, who had lost her hearing through an attack of scarlet fever when she was four and a half years old. The child had been sent to Germany for a course of many years but there had been little in the way of results except that she had learned lip reading. Graham Bell was not engaged to undertake her tuition but he instructed her teacher in his methods and particularly in Visible Speech. He went often to the Hubbard house and watched her lessons.

Mabel Hubbard, who was growing up into a very lovely girl, was destined to play a highly important and lasting part in the life of Alexander Graham Bell.

These were among the highlights of his early experiences which he poured into the ears of his parents as soon as he arrived on his vacations. He would take a cab at the station and drive out, making a characteristic entrance by coming without warning or ceremony through the long french window into the drawing room. The first intimation they would have of his arrival would be the sound of his voice calling cheerfully: "Here I am. And what stories I have to tell you!"

2

It is made clear in some of the letters he sent home that his main interest during the first years in Boston was in perfecting his multiple telegraph signal. On March 18, 1875, he wrote to his parents from 292 Essex Street, Salem:

I left Boston last Sunday and called at the office of the Western Union on Monday. Mr. Orton and Mr. Prescott both devoted a large portion of their time discussing with me the whole plan from its theoretical point of view. Mr. Smith, the manager of the experimental room was absent from town but was telegraphed for. He replied that he could not come until next morning. Tuesday forenoon we had the batteries connected and I tuned up my instruments. They went like clockwork. I have come to the conclusion that by a happy chance they are much more perfect than I thought at first. The signals were as clear, sharp and rapid as with the ordinary Morse sounder. I connected two Transmitters and two Receivers on only one line and two messages were sent simultaneously.

We had 100 cells of a battery, and all went well on our artificial circuit. Mr. Prescott then said he would like to see them tried on a real live wire. He telegraphed to Philadelphia to have two wires crossed there so as to give us (practically) a continuous wire from New York to Philadelphia and back. The electro-magnets I employed were not intended for trial on a long line. They were wound with coarse wire and the "resistance" was only "3 ohms." Ordinary electro-magnets for actual service on a line have a resistance of about 200 to 600 ohms. None of us, therefore, expected the instruments to work without stronger magnets. But they *did work*.

The signals, though feeble, came sharply and concisely through the 200 miles of live wire. I suggested trying stronger magnets, so Mr. Prescott ordered the instruments to be taken to the workshop and stronger magnets to be placed on them. They were to be ready in the afternoon, so I went out to dinner and returned in a couple of hours.

Rest will form subject for next letter.

With fond love,
Your affectionate son,
Aleck.

Salem, May 24

Dear Papa and Mama:

I am so immersed in telegraphy and science that I find it impossible to write freely about anything else, but I feel that at the present time you can scarcely be inclined to listen to anything I have to say on such subjects.

Since I gave up professional work and devoted myself exclusively to telegraphy, I have been steadily gaining health and strength, and am now in a fit state to encounter Mr. Gray or anyone else. The patents that have been granted to me without opposition are,—

1st. The principle of converting a vibratory motion into a permanent make or break of a local circuit.

2nd. The special form of "vibratory circuit breaker" put in illustration.

3rd. The autograph telegraph.

The autograph telegraph is rapidly approaching completion. Already I can copy handwriting *quite legibly,* though not yet neatly. The rate of transmission by my instrument will be exactly ten times more rapid than "Bakewell's Autograph Telegraph," in which the rate is 300 letters per minute. When 3000 letters per minute can be sent, my telegraph will be the most *rapid* as well as the *cheapest*. .

Every moment of my time is devoted to study of electricity and to experiments. The subject broadens. I think that the transmission of the human voice is much more nearly at hand than I had supposed. However, this is kept in the background just now, as every effort is to be made to complete the autograph telegraph arrangement, so as to have it used on some line.

The two patents for the transmission of musical notes are not decided yet. I can't understand why the Interference should not have been declared before this. Here are some of the late discoveries: 1. The current from one of my instruments passed through an iron wire causes a musical note to issue from the wire. 2. The same effect is produced by passing the current through a piece of carbon. 3. Ditto when it is forced through the plumbago of an ordinary lead pencil. No similar effects noted yet with copper, brass, or mercury.

A still more curious phenomenon is the following: Two thin strips of brass are connected with the wires coming from my Transmitting instrument T, and from the Battery. On holding A to my ear I hear nothing, but the moment that I touch B with my finger, a musical note is heard to proceed from A.

Truly, the more I study electricity and magnetism the more I feel the truth of Hamlet's saying, "There are more things," etc. I fear that this telegraphic business may force me to remain the greater part of the summer here, but I cannot tell yet, so many details have to be worked out. My inexperience in such matters is a great drawback. However, Morse conquered his electrical difficulties although he was only a painter, and I don't intend to give in either until all is completed.

> With dear love
> > Yr affectionate son,
> > > Aleck.

The following letter indicates that, although his work was still tending in one direction, the Multiple Telegraph, he was at the same time aware of results which promised still greater things, the transmission of the human voice over wires. In the following letter, dated March 18, 1875, he tells the story of a fateful interview with Professor Henry of the Smithsonian Institution in

Alexander Graham Bell in his student days in Edinburgh.

The inventor at the age of twenty-five, taken in a room of the Bell home on Tutelo Heights.

A self-portrait done in water color by Mrs. Alexander Melville
Bell, the inventor's mother.

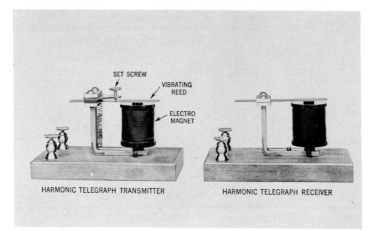

SET SCREW

VIBRATING REED

ELECTRO MAGNET

HARMONIC TELEGRAPH TRANSMITTER

HARMONIC TELEGRAPH RECEIVER

The Multiple Telegraph, on which Mr. Bell was also at work. It was on this instrument that on June 2, 1875, in Boston, he heard the twang transmitted electrically by undulating current.

(*Opposite, above*) The triple mouthpiece used at Brantford in the three important tests. (*Below*) The iron-box telephone over which he received at Paris the first long-distance telephone call.

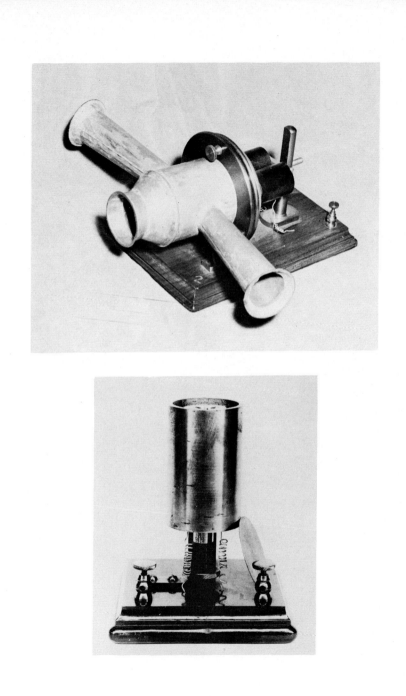

Professor Alexander Melville Bell, the father of the inventor, taken in 1878.

A photograph of Alexander Graham Bell at the age of forty-three.

The Bell Memorial in the heart of the city of Brantford.

The house in Edinburgh, at 13 Hope Street, where Alexander
Graham Bell spent his boyhood.

The homestead on Tutelo Heights, taken on March 9, 1906. Here Mr. Bell is accompanied by his elder daughter, Mrs. Gilbert Grosvenor.

The inventor on the front veranda of the homestead, on the afternoon of the same day.

The birches at the rear of the property, overlooking the Grand River. It was here the young inventor spent much of his time in regaining his health.

(*Opposite*) Two interior views of the homestead at Brantford.

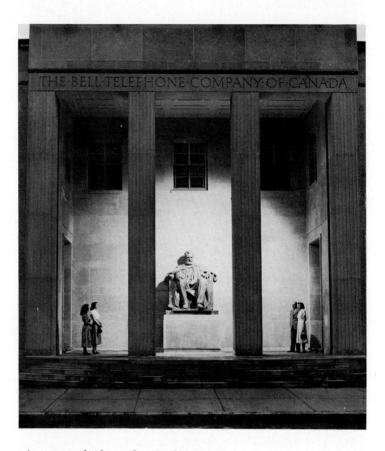

A statue of Alexander Graham Bell in the front entrance of telephone headquarters in Brantford. This was unveiled by Mrs. Grosvenor on June 18, 1949.

(*Opposite, above*) The Bell home as it appeared in 1949. (*Below*) The monument erected by the Government of Canada to mark it as a site of national importance.

The grounds at the rear of the homestead. There has been a steady erosion of soil and much of the original property is now lost.

Washington. In later years Mr. Bell would speak of this interview as the turning point in his career. The encouragement given him by Professor Henry spurred him on to renewed efforts to achieve his great objective.

Dear Papa and Mama:

I have just returned from my trip to New York thoroughly worn out. Found your letters of the 14th inst. awaiting me. I am now beginning to realize the cares and anxieties of being an inventor. In order to complete the apparatus as thoroughly as possible, I have decided to give up all professional work for some weeks. I have put off all pupils and classes until 12th of April. Flesh and blood could not stand much longer such a strain as I have had upon me. Professional work is all in confusion, and the only way is to cut the Gordian knot and throw up everything until the end is achieved. I long to write full accounts to you, and I have delayed writing in order to give a connected narrative of the whole. You seem to think my anxieties are over, when in truth they are really only beginning.

Before entering upon explanations, let me ask you first to hunt over all my old letters that you have preserved, for everything bearing on the Telegraph. Forward to me at once as evidence. I must take action at once in regard to foreign patents. Will you or uncle help me in this?

What I would like is this: I have written to my

lawyers in Washington to make application for foreign patents on my own responsibility.

Should I prove unable to pay for these applications at once, will you help me? While these applications are being got out I shall write to the Herdmans offering them a share if they will take the pecuniary burden of any interference, etc. that may arise abroad from Mr. Gray. Should they decline— which I should think unlikely—I should, of course, relinquish a foreign contest.

Whenever I am free to dispose of my interest in the invention I shall do so, and then you may expect to see Visible Speech go ahead. I can then take up the electric motor, which I think as valuable an idea as this telegraph.

. . . Now, to resume telegraphy. When I was in Washington I had a letter of introduction to Professor Henry, who is the Tyndall of America. I found on inquiry at the Institute of Technology that some of the points I had discovered in relation to the application of acoustics to telegraphy had been previously discovered by him. I thought I would, therefore, explain all the experiments, and ascertain what was new and what was old. He listened with an unmoved countenance, but with evident interest to all, but when I related an experiment that at first sight seems unimportant I was startled at the sudden interest manifested.

I told him that on passing an intermittent current of electricity through an empty helix of insulated copper wire, a noise could be heard proceeding from the coil, similar to that heard from the telephone. He started up, said, "Is that so? Will you allow me, Mr. Bell, to repeat your experiments, and publish them to the world through the Smithsonian Institution, of course giving you the credit of the discoveries?"

I said it would give me extreme pleasure, and added that I had apparatus in Washington, and could show him the experiments at any time. He asked if I could do it *then,* if he went with me, and I told him I had everything in readiness at Mr. Hubbard's house. He said, "I will go with you now. Have you a carriage here?" I had not, and so he put on his coat and was about to order his carriage, when I offered to save him the trouble of going out on such a raw, damp day, by bringing the apparatus to the Smithsonian Institution. (He was suffering from a cold, and besides is very aged,—I believe about eighty years old.)

We appointed noon next day for the experiment. I set the instrument working and he sat at a table for a long time with the empty coil of wire against his ear listening to the sound. I felt so much encouraged by his interest to ask his advice about the apparatus I have designed for the transmission of the human voice by telegraph. I explained the idea and said, "What would you advise me to do, publish it and let others work it out, or attempt to solve the problem myself?" He said he thought it was "the germ of a great invention," and advised me to work it myself instead of publishing it. I said that I recognized the fact that there were mechanical difficulties in the way that rendered the plan impracticable at the present time. I added that I felt that I had not the electrical knowledge necessary to overcome the difficulties. His laconic answer was, "GET IT."

I cannot tell you how much these two words have encouraged me. I live too much in an atmosphere of discouragement for scientific pursuits. Good —— is unfortunately one of the *cui bono* people, and is too much in the habit of looking at the dark side of things. Such a chimerical idea as telegraphing *vocal sounds* would indeed to *most minds* seem scarcely feasible enough to spend time in working over. . . . I believe however, that this is feasible, and that I have got the cue to the solution of the problem.

Professor Henry seemed to be much interested in what I told him, and cross-questioned me about my past life, and specially wanted to know where I had studied physics. . . .

By this time Graham Bell had reached the stage where he was certain he could obtain patents on his discoveries in the field of multiple telegraphy, a view which was encouraged by his lawyers. The "Mr. Gray," whose name begins to crop up in the various letters, was Elisha Gray, who had secured patents in the field of telegraphy and was known to be engaged on experiments on the transmission of the voice.

The Western Union [Aleck wrote home on March 5, 1875] is probably the largest corporate body that has ever existed.

It controls more miles of telegraph wires than there are in the whole of Europe! It was therefore important to have my instruments in good shape. I did my best by getting nitric acid and sulphuric acid to get the cells I had in working order. I sawed a large carbon in two, borrowed a couple of slop-basins and had the whole in working order just *half a minute* before Mr. Orton made his appearance. The instruments by good luck never worked better. Mr. Orton was very much interested, and said he would like to see me again but had to go to New York that night.

Two days afterward, I was in the Capitol seeing the Senate, when a gentleman came in and tapped me on the shoulder. It was Mr. Orton. He told me that the Western Union would be glad to give me every facility in perfecting my instruments, and he gave me a hearty invitation to take my apparatus to

New York, and I should have the assistance of their best electricians.

They have a special experimental room, and have at instant command thousands of cells of battery, and thousands of miles of *real* live wire to test with.

Mr. Orton said further, that he wished me to distinctly understand that the Western Union had no interest in Mr. Gray or his invention. This is very encouraging. Mr. Orton had previously seen Gray's apparatus, and yet he came forward to take up mine.

In regard to the patents: My lawyers, Pollak and Bailey, found on examination at the Patent Office, that I had developed the idea so much further than Gray had done that they have applied for three distinct patents, in only one of which I come into collision with Gray. The first patent covers the principle of "Multiple Telegraphy," basing my claim upon the instruments exhibited. (These instruments require *two* lines, an up-line and down-line.)

The second patent covers the principle of using the *Induced Current,* so as to permit a single wire to be employed.

The third patent is for a "vibratory circuit breaker" for the purpose of converting the vibratory motion of my Receiving Instrument into a permanent *make* or *break* of a local circuit.

By this arrangement I can make a receiver work any instrument whatever that can be moved by electro-magnetism and it is developed into a curious form of "Autograph Telegraph" by means of which an autograph message or picture may be almost instantly copied. The copy is made in ordinary ink and on ordinary paper.

My lawyers were at first doubtful whether the examiners would declare an interference between me and Gray, as Gray's apparatus had been there for so long a time.

They feared I had but a poor chance, and my spirits at once fell to zero. They said it would be difficult to convince them that I had not copied. When, however, they saw the "Autograph Telegraph" developed from the idea of multiple telegraphy, they at once said that that was a good proof of independent invention, as Gray had no such idea. It further turned out that an examiner in the Patent Office (not, however, of electrical inventions) is a deaf-mute, and knows me personally and by reputation, and could surely vouch for the fact of my being incapable of copying Gray.

Another fortunate circumstance was this. That the very examiner into whose hands this will come happened to be in Mr. Pollak's office one day when I called, so that I had a long interview with him, and I can't help thinking that he must have been convinced of my independent conception of the whole thing.

After making out our specifications, and examining into the whole thing, Mr. Pollak said, "You have a good case." The last words he said when I left were, "You need not fear, we shall pull you through all right."

Whenever Gray's lawyer heard that I was in town he applied to the Patent Office to complete Gray's patents, and thus force me to a law suit.

The examiners, however, could not act in the matter for ten days, so that gave me time to get my application in in time. I am now waiting for the decision of the examining board. They will probably declare an interference. Then I shall have to have witnesses examined and prove priority.

The invention could not have come out at any better time than the present. I shall explain how.

There are two rival telegraph companies in America; The Western Union and the "Pacific Line."

The Western Union have hitherto enjoyed a monopoly. But last year a man invented a method of sending four messages simultaneously along the same wire, and the Pacific Telegraph Company bought his patent for seven hundred and fifty thousand dollars ($750,000).

The result has been that the Pacific Company has been able to reduce their prices so as to compete successfully with the Western Union.

Now my invention comes along as a means by

which thirty or forty messages may be sent simultaneously, and by which intermediate stations may communicate with one another. If the Western Union take it up it would enable them to recover lost ground. At all events it is evidently a good time to bring out the invention. I visited the Western Union telegraph headquarters to New York on my way here. I have made arrangements to spend Saturday and Sunday every week in New York at the West. Un. Building.

I am to have the assistance of Mr. Prescott (the author of the book you have on Telegraphy), so now I feel that all is plain sailing if I can prove priority.

Here is Boston. Much love.

Aleck.

3

The family at home in Brantford did not know much about electricity. The telegraph to them was a relatively new wonder by which messages could be sent over wires by a code of signals. They knew that young Aleck had in his mind certain methods by which the telegraph could be made more wonderful and useful although they did not understand how it was to be done.

But the telephone was a different matter. All members of the Bell family were dedicated to proper speech and the assistance of the unfortunates who lacked the power to hear or speak. The telephone was a greater piece of magic, for it aimed to transmit the human voice over wires. It was this dream of their talented son's in which they were almost passionately interested. Of course, they listened when he told them of his Multiple Telegraph and tried to understand. But their first question on his arrivals was almost certainly "What of the telephone?" It is no exaggeration to say that from the moment of his return in early summer until it became necessary for him to pack up in late autumn to return, the telephone monopolized their conversation, filled their minds, and shared their dreams. They were impatient, no doubt, of the long time it took to see friends in the city, of their inability to pick up a curious instrument and talk to a neighbor without moving from the porch at Melville House. Graham Bell himself continued, no doubt, to give thought to the final improvements on his new telegraph and perhaps to work on some phase of it which did not seem perfect. But it is in no sense a distortion of the known facts to say that in Brantford he turned at once to the telephone and lived for the period of his visit with that favorite dream.

A proof of this can be found in the diary which Professor Melville Bell kept during these important periods. He was a busy man and not given to prosy descriptions or long-winded dissertations. It is probable that, before going to bed each night, he reached down the book in which he was recording his impressions and preserved the essence of what had happened that day in a sentence, a phrase, or even a single word. His was probably the most terse and cryptic diary ever written by human hand. It goes a long way, nevertheless, to prove the assertions made above. There were some references to the telegraph, particularly in the earliest years, but in almost all cases the sentence, the phrase, or the single word had to do with the dream that was close to their hearts.

Here are some extracts:

September 7, 1874: "Aleck full of schemes."

December 1874: "Al's experiments described."

The first specific reference to the telephone is found on December 26, 1874: "Long talk on multiple telegraphy and speech transmission. Al. sanguine."

The word "telephone" was first used on December 29, three days later: "Talking half the night. Motors and telephone."

September 12, 1875: "Telephone talk. Wonderful!"

December 29, 1875: "Agreement entered into with G. [Honorable George Brown] and J. G. Brown."

March 26, 1876, in a letter written home while visiting his son: "Busy testing telephone.—Success."

July 24, 1876, when the crucial days were approaching fast: "Alec arrived by the study window."

August 4, 1876: "Gentlemen's supper. 23 guests. Telephone to Brantford. A line was run along the fence for the occasion."

To these brief notes of Melville Bell's may be added the most significant statement that the inventor gave on the stand during patent hearings, many years later. He was telling what had happened at Brantford on July 26, 1874. He was searching for a method to make a current of electricity vary in density as the air varies during the production of sound.

"While this problem was in my mind," he explained, "I was carrying on experiments with the phonautograph constructed from the human ear which Dr. Blake had prepared for me. I do not think that the membrane of this ear could have been half an inch in diameter and it appeared to be as thin as tissue paper. I was much struck by the disproportion in weight between the membrane and the bones that were moved by it; and it occurred to me that if such a thin and delicate membrane could move bones that were, relatively to it, very massive indeed, why should not a larger and stouter membrane be able to move a piece of steel in the manner I desired? *At once the conception of a membrane speaking telephone became complete in my mind; for I saw that a similar instrument to that used as a transmitter could also be employed as a receiver— The arrangement thus conceived in the summer of 1874 was substantially similar to that shown in Fig. 7 of my patent of March 7, 1876.*"

Melville Bell might be laconic in his diary but the talks he thus summarized were long and full. When the father was called as a witness some years later during the patent suits, he was asked if his son talked much about the invention. He replied, "My chief difficulty in remembering what took place on any one visit was from the fact that he was constantly talking *about the telephone and that he talked of little else.*"

4

The most telling evidence that work on the telephone was largely reserved for the periods spent in Brantford is found in the arrangements which Graham Bell made with his partners in Boston.

In the fall of 1874 Thomas Sanders came to the young inventor with a promise to supply him with money in return for a share in his patent rights. Shortly afterward Gardiner Greene Hubbard made a similar proposition. So, on February 27, 1875, an agreement among the three men was drawn up and signed. The partnership, based on this agreement, became known later as The Bell Patent Association. The first result was that on March 6 an application was filed in the Patent Office at Washington for Patent No. 161,739, for Improvement in Transmitters and Receivers for Electrical Telegraphs. The patent was duly issued on April 6 of that year.

Graham Bell never wavered in his loyalty to the two men who backed him so generously and yet the formation of the partnership might have had the effect of delaying the invention of the telephone. Both of the partners were convinced that his chance for success lay in completing his work on the Multiple Telegraph. The telephone, in their minds, was a secondary consideration, and a highly speculative one. They were so strongly of this opinion that the agreement signed between them made no mention of the telephone. "The said Bell has invented certain new and useful methods and apparatus for telegraphing" was the way the document read.

It was not a desire for quick financial returns which actuated Mr. Hubbard in urging the young Scot to devote himself to his telegraphic experiments. Rather it was an expression of his belief that Bell's improvements in the operation of the telegraph were proven successes and that it was a matter of common sense to complete them first. The telephone could come later. It seems certain that Mr. Sanders shared these views. The latter continued to pour money into the company with a free hand. Ultimately his investment reached the figure of $110,000 before he received any returns.

It may be thought that the words "telegraph" and "telephone" were at the time interchangeable words. It was not the intent of the agreement, however, to cover both meanings, according to Mr. William Chauncy Langdon, who was historical librarian of the American Telephone & Telegraph Company. In a brief story of the early days, published first in July 1923 in the *Bell Telephone Quarterly*, Mr. Langdon said: "It was either an inadvertent or a deliberate discrimination in favor of the telegraph. Mr. Sanders and Mr. Hubbard had both formerly believed that the Multiple Telegraph was the invention that would prove to be the profitable one."

Even after the successful tests of the telephone conducted in Brantford removed all doubts as to the possibilities of the new instrument, the two partners were not of the opinion that they had a share in it. There was never the faintest trace of friction among the three men and the disclaimer on the part of Messrs. Hubbard and Sanders was an evidence of their generous attitude. They did not want to assert a right which they honestly considered doubtful.

It was Graham Bell himself who insisted that they were entitled to a share in the telephone. He is on record to this effect:

> My understanding always was that the speaking telephone was included in the inventions that belonged to the Messrs. Hubbard and Sanders from the autumn of 1874 but I found at a later period that they had not this idea, which might account for the little encouragement I received to spend time on experiments relating to it. Even as late as 1876, when the telephone was an assured success, Mr. Hubbard generously offered to relinquish to me all right and title to that invention, as he was inclined to think it was outside our original understanding.

When court records are filled with the wrangling of partners over the division of profits, it is most refreshing to find how thoroughly these men, who held an important issue in their hands, trusted one another and leaned over backward to be fair.

Chapter Eight

The Key Is Found

1

THE clue to great inventions often comes like a ray of light cutting suddenly and unexpectedly through the gloom. Sometimes the inventor sees the truth hidden behind some casually accepted detail of everyday life, as in the often told examples of Newton and the apple and Watt watching the lid of the kettle. More frequently the final result is arrived at by a logical development, each step leading to the next until the inevitable success is achieved. The telephone seems to fall into the last as well as the bolt-in-the-blue classification.

Through all the discord which has arisen over the story of the telephone, one fact seems to be generally accepted: the key to its inception was found in Brantford during the vacation that Graham Bell spent at Tutelo Heights in 1874. He had come home very tired.

Sleepless nights and irregular meals, together with incessant labor, had taken their toll. It was clear to his
anxious parents that he had lost much of the ground
gained during the first years in Canada.

He proceeded to sleep long hours, to rest during the
day in his hammock on the edge of the bluff, and to
enjoy good meals. For a brief period he allowed his
mind to lie fallow. And then it came to him, the idea he
had been seeking so long, the brilliant solution which
scientists in all parts of civilization had been pursuing
with equal intensity.

He had been studying the phonautograph in connection with his efforts to complete his Multiple Telegraph.
A phonautograph was a sound writer, a hollow cylinder
with a membrane stretched over one end. A stylus was
attached to the same end and, when words were spoken
into the tube at the other end, the stylus would move
in sympathy with the vibrations of the membrane. The
result was a series of lines inscribed on smoked glass
which conveyed the meaning of the words. The thought
which suddenly flooded Bell's mind was that the human
ear was the most perfect instrument in all nature for
detecting and recording sound. What if a membrane receiver could be modeled closely after the ear? What
miracles would result? Was it possible that sounds sent
over a steel wire would register in the form of speech
in a receiver so designed?

One version often repeated is that Graham Bell was

lying in his hammock when this inspiration came to him, or at any rate stretched out on the "sofa seat." He sat straight upright but for several moments made no further move. He stared unseeingly at the serpentine course of the Grand River, his thoughts racing, his mind filled with the dazzling possibilities he perceived. Then he got slowly to his feet, retrieved a book which had fallen to the ground, and turned toward the garden. For the first few steps he went slowly, then his whole frame was galvanized into activity and he raced for the house.

His mind being an orderly one, and not prone to accept new ideas blindly, he may have diluted his exuberance with some qualifying thoughts. "Is it too good to be true? A magneto telephone! But can the voice create strong enough electrical impulses all by itself?"

He had the vision now. Could it be developed for practical uses?

Another version is that he was seated at the piano when that epochal conception entered his mind. His parents paid no attention when the music ceased abruptly. There was nothing new in that. He would often stop and sit for a time in perfect silence before beginning to strike single notes at intervals as though testing the exact sounds.

Being a composer at heart, he would undoubtedly under these circumstances apply himself again to the keyboard and indulge in triumphant improvisation before shouting loudly to his father that he thought he had it at last.

Or again it may have been that the solution suggested itself during one of the inevitable nighttime vigils, when the creative mind will sometimes stumble over the truth.

At every stage of his long and creative life Graham Bell remained a believer in orderly development, sometimes going over ground already familiar to experts in order to be sure himself of each step. But he was also a man of quick impulses. It would be contrary to his nature to sit back in idleness and do nothing about his revolutionary conviction of the need to copy the human ear. The first step, clearly, would be to examine the composition of the ear and the way it operated. But where could the necessary specimen be obtained in Brantford?

The need for a real hospital would not be met in that city for another ten years and at the time of the Bell experiments a large building, formerly the residence of Mr. James Wilks (a handsome structure, sometimes referred to as the Baronial Hall), served the purpose. It was doubtful if anything much was done there in the clinical line, and certainly no youthful layman would be allowed to take a human ear from a deceased patient, to be used for experiments.

I have heard from several widely dispersed sources that young Mr. Bell conducted experiments with a hog's ear. William Sloane is on record with a story that it was a dog's ear he was using. The truth seems to be that Dr. Clarence J. Blake of Boston obtained a human ear, which he gave to the young inventor in 1874, and that the latter took the specimen to Brantford that summer, to be used in a phonautograph. It is quite possible that he kept this a secret and gave it out that he was using the ear of an animal to prevent gossip.

Chapter Nine

The Second Great Step

1

GRAHAM BELL returned to Boston after his 1874 vacation in Brantford convinced that the membrane telephone, based on the structure of the ear, was the key to the problem. But he was still weighed down with serious problems. His two good friends in Boston, Thomas Sanders and Gardiner Greene Hubbard, who were making it possible for him to continue his experiments, showed an interest in the great idea which had come to him at Tutelo Heights but their chief concern was still the Multiple Telegraph, on which patents had been secured. They felt it was no more than sound common sense to complete the task which was so well along rather than to be lured away by something new because it was more spectacular.

To complicate matters still further, Graham Bell and Mabel Hubbard were very much in love. There is noth-

ing in the record to indicate that Mr. Hubbard opposed
the match at the start but, because the young inventor
was likely to become his son-in-law, a new note was introduced into their relationship. Mr. Hubbard was
a sound man of business and he was not likely to favor
giving his daughter in marriage to a man who seemed
inclined to be visionary and lacking in stability, even
though he might be the natural genius of the age. Graham Bell realized this so completely that he regretted
the need to depend on his backers. Although he was in
serious financial straits, he could not bring himself to go
back to Mr. Hubbard and say that he needed more
money. He realized, further, that the stand taken by his
backers was a right and proper one. He should be ready
to do everything in his power to bring his telegraphic
invention to a stage of sufficient perfection and stability
to sell the rights to the Western Union Telegraph Company before he pursued further the grander possibilities
of the telephone.

The trouble with the Multiple Telegraph, at this
stage, was that he could not maintain all parts in a necessary perfection of operation. To send any number of
messages simultaneously over a single wire, it was
necessary to have a transmitter for each and to provide
a receiver adjusted to the exact pitch of the transmitter.
The merest variation would throw everything out of
kilter. To explain the difficulty in everyday terms, it was
like having a number of people walking close together
along parallel straight lines. If one fell out of step it was

inevitable that the rest would be instantly jostled out of position also, and that chaos would result.

Knowing that his backers expected him to solve this difficulty with the telegraph, young Graham Bell returned to Boston in a state of mind which carried a certain measure of despair. He knew that the continuous need for adjusting each transmitter to its own individual receiver was a problem he could solve only by finding some new stabilizing element. The solution had not been found. All he could hope for was that it would emerge finally from his continuous experimentation.

Was ever man in a more trying situation than this? A great white light had flooded his mind during those days of recuperation at Tutelo Heights. He knew it was the answer to what he had been seeking. And yet he must lay it aside, keep it muffled away and under cover, and postpone all efforts to develop it into concrete form until he had completed another task which he was beginning to think might be beyond him.

No doubt he said to himself many times: "Why did I ever let myself be diverted from the work I was intended by nature to do? I was a born teacher. I liked the work. If I had continued to give my full time to my classes, I would be earning enough today to support a wife. I could go with a clear conscience to ask for the hand of the girl I love. Should I not give up all this desperate, this frenzied probing into the mysteries of nature and go back to teaching again?"

He knew, of course, whenever these thoughts crossed his mind, that it was impossible to return to the sedate and tranquil role of a teacher. The vision had not been given him to toss away. It might very well be that out of the conception which had come to him there would be a great change in the world. The slow pace of human communication was costing much in the way of lives lost, because help could not be summoned in time. Disasters were not prevented, and causes were lost, and much additional unhappiness was added to the lot of man because word of things took days and weeks and months to circulate instead of seconds and minutes. Being a man of imaginative cast and prophetic mind, Alexander Graham Bell knew all this; and so he realized he could never turn away from the responsibility which had been offered him. He must accept the delays and disappointments and misunderstandings to which every pioneer is subjected. Others could carry on the work of teaching sufferers from defective speech but only Alexander Graham Bell could give the telephone to the world.

The most persistent distress he felt was that because of this it was uncertain that he would ever marry Mabel Hubbard. He loved her so much that he suffered intensely over all the obstacles which fate seemed to be putting in his way. There was, in the first place, the wealth of the Hubbards. They lived in a large and handsome house on Brattle Street in Cambridge. It stood well back in a deep garden, with a stable in the rear. There was a staff of servants and when the family went out in the carriage of an afternoon, they rode behind a coachman in livery.

There were four girls in the family, all of them pretty and vivacious, Gertrude, Mabel, Berta, and Grace. It must be acknowledged that, although he had not yet attained greatness or fame, he had some of the idiosyncrasies of genius. His formal manners and his precision of speech amused the younger sisters and they teased their gentle sister Mabel about her suitor. Bell was sometimes ill at ease when he paid a call there. Once, after ringing the doorbell and receiving no immediate response, he decided to withdraw quietly and not come back. But, most fortunately, Mabel herself opened the door (perhaps she had been watching for him) before he could get away. The unmistakable welcome in her eyes drew him back.

It has been said that Mr. Hubbard finally told the young inventor he would never give his consent to his marriage with Mabel unless he gave up "all this nonsense" about hearing speech over wires. The source of this story is not given and so its authenticity may be doubted. There can be no doubt at all, however, that the diffident suitor feared it might come to that. If he persisted in his efforts to make a telephone, which sometimes must have seemed as elusive as a quest for the philosophers' stone, or if he failed to make his Multiple Telegraph behave itself (as someone put it), he might reasonably expect that the head of the Hubbard family would show him the door.

Fortunately Mabel was as much in love with him as he was with her, and she had no intention of allowing anything, not even a paternal veto, to come between them. This he did not know when he returned to Boston in the autumn of 1874. And so he carried a pain in his heart which disturbed him more than the troubles he was having in his own little world of science.

2

It has already been said that Graham Bell had one reservation about the use of equipment fashioned on the human ear. Would it be possible for the voice to create electrical impulses strong enough to travel for long distances over wire?

The answer to that was found soon after his return to Boston and it came through an accident in the course of his experiments on the telegraph. His faith in the Multiple Telegraph, if it had ever seriously waned, had returned full force, as witness a letter he sent to "Dear Papa and Mama" on May 24, 1875. He included in it a list of the patents which had been granted to him "without opposition." "Every moment of my time," he went on to say, "is devoted to study of electricity and to experiments. The subject broadens. I think that the trans-

146

mission of the human voice is much more nearly at hand than I had supposed. However, this is kept in the background just now, as every effort is to be made to complete the autograph arrangement, so as to have it used on some line."

When he wrote that letter he had no conception that in a very short time indeed he would have the answer to all his doubts. It came about through the unending efforts he was making to get the "bugs," to use a modern term, out of the Multiple Telegraph.

Back in Boston he made an important acquaintance. He was having all his apparatus prepared at the electrical plant of Charles Williams and on one occasion had to take back a piece of mechanism he had found imperfect. It had been the work of a young electrical worker named Thomas A. Watson. Disregarding office rules, Bell went straight to Watson's bench to explain what was wrong.

In later years Watson, who was to have his share in the glory and the wealth, wrote a volume of reminiscences which he called *Exploring Life* and in it he gave his first impression of Alexander Graham Bell, as he saw him that day. "A tall, slender, quick-motioned man with a pale face, black side-whiskers and drooping moustache, big nose and a high, sloping forehead crowned with bushy black hair . . . The tone of his voice seemed vividly to color his words. His clear, crisp articulation delighted me and made other men's speech seem uncouth. When he learned of my interest in speech tones, he was surprised and pleased and gave me some of his father's books on elocution."

Watson, it developed, had started to work in the plant at an early age, operating a hand lathe and being paid the handsome wage of five dollars a week. He rather diffidently confessed to Bell that he was hopeful of becoming an inventor himself. Whenever an idea occurred to him, he would make a note on a card and put it away in a pocket. At the time he was carrying around a great sheaf of them.

Is heated glass a conductor?
Pills to improve the voice?
What sort of vibration is made by a hissing sound?
Is it electricity that keeps clouds in air?

Young Watson was so helpful to Bell that finally he was assigned to give all his time to the young Scot. They worked on the Multiple Telegraph, laboring day and night. The obstacles in the way of perfection could not, seemingly, be overcome. The multiple messages dispatched simultaneously over one wire still stepped on each other's toes, as it were. As Watson had no keenness of sound perception, Bell had to assume all the labor of tuning and changing and retuning. He would hold the receiver reed to his ear, as Watson wrote later, "to hear in the magnet the whine of the intermittent current coming from the distant transmitter." It was a continuous succession of tightening and loosening screws to get both ends into absolute harmony.

One evening, when all the delicate adjustments had gone awry, Bell shook his head in despair. It seemed impossible to make the thing work.

"Watson," he said, "I want to tell you of another idea which I think will surprise you."

Watson was so impressed by what he was told that he always remembered the exact words. In the course of time he set them down in his autobiography.

"If I could make a current of electricity vary in intensity," explained Alexander Graham Bell, "precisely as air varies in density during the production of a sound, I would be able to transmit speech electrically."

This remarkable prediction was spoken in the resonant voice which Watson admired so much; which had driven him, in fact, into efforts to achieve the same fine tones by going out alone on Sundays into the woods in order to recite and declaim.

In his autobiography, Watson has told the story of the great moment in full detail. It was on the afternoon of June 2, 1875, a distressingly sultry day. The two young men were hard at it, Bell in one room and Watson in another, sixty feet away. Bell was engaged in his continuous labor of tuning one transmitter after another. Suddenly, under Watson's intent eye, one of the transmitting springs ceased to vibrate. He was sure it had become stuck and so he plucked at it to get it free again.

Most unexpectedly he heard Bell calling to him from the other room, in an excited voice.

"What did you do?"

A moment later the young Scot appeared in the doorway. His eyes were shining as, perhaps, they had never shone before. He repeated: "What did you do then? Don't change a thing! Let me see!"

Watson's story proceeds as follows: "I showed him that it was very simple. The make-and-break points of the transmitter spring I was trying to start had become welded together, so that when I snapped the spring the circuit had remained unbroken while that strip of magnetized steel, by its vibrations over the pole of the magnet, was generating that marvellous conception of Bell's—a current of electricity that varied in intensity precisely as the air was varying in density within hearing distance of the spring."

That was all that Bell needed to know. Something new in electricity had been brought about, a current to which he later gave the descriptive name of undulatory. He knew at once that this undulatory current would accomplish what the interrupted current had failed to do.

What had happened was not entirely a surprise to the young inventor. This is clear when considered in the light of the evidence that he gave in the final patent hearing, which has already been quoted.

Neither of the zealous pair had any doubt of the importance of the discovery. Watson wrote in his memoirs, "Bell was hearing for the first time in human history the tones and overtones of a sound transmitted by electricity."

Fearing that the new current might be an accidental effect, the pair devoted the rest of the day, far on into the hours of darkness, to repeating the process. They used every tuning spring in the shop, one after another. The result was always the same. They continued to hear, faint but unmistakable, the same voice-shaped electrical undulations. It was as though they were listening to the faraway voice of the spheres.

Finally Bell sat down at his desk and drew up plans for an instrument that he wanted made the next day. Watson describes it as follows: "I was to construct a wooden plane on which was mounted one of Bell's harmonic receivers, a tightly stretched parchment drumhead to the centre of which the free end of the receiver was fashioned; and a mouthpiece arranged to direct the voice against the other end of the drumhead. It was designed to force the reed to follow the vibrations of the voice."

Some years later, in speaking of this, Professor Bell said: "Orders were given at once to construct the membrane telephone that was conceived in Brantford in 1874."

Sleep was out of the question for Bell after Watson had departed to catch the last train for his home in the suburbs. Finally he sat down and wrote a letter to Mr. Hubbard, thinking, no doubt, how much better and easier it would be if he could speak into a transmitter and hear his backer's voice respond from the other end. He began by saying, "I have accidentally made a discovery of the very greatest importance."

Chapter Ten

A Voice Speaks
in an Emperor's Ear

1

P. T. BARNUM had ushered in the period of high-
powered press-agentry many years before, but
Philadelphia would have had little of the kind to win
attention for the Centennial Exhibition in 1876 if the
only monarch in America had not elected to attend.
Pedro II, emperor of Brazil, popularly known as Dom
Pedro, had been in the United States before, traveling
incognito, or so it was said. He was favorably known in
all the Americas for the liberality of his views and the
many enlightened things he had done for the people of
his country. He had led a campaign for the abolition of
slavery and had earned the enmity of the landed classes
thereby. During a widespread epidemic he had gone out
and served as a nurse to the sick, running the risk of

infection. He was deeply interested in education. In
fact, he had been responsible for so many good things
that the people wanted to raise a bronze statue to him.
Dom Pedro asked that the money be used instead for
an ambitious school-building campaign which he had
launched.

He was the very model of a modern constitutional
monarch and it was surprising that some years later the
Brazilian people, looking about them and seeing all
their neighbors enjoying (not quite the word, in view
of all the upsets and revolutions) the fruits of elective
rule, decided that monarchic government was out-
dated. He was dethroned in 1889 by a military junta
and died two years later in Europe. Little was heard
about him during the last unpleasant years, so it may be
assumed that he continued to exercise his liking for
anonymity.

Dom Pedro came to the Centennial with a large
party, including his consort, Dona Thereza, in the three
largest battleships in the Brazilian Navy. Philadelphia
welcomed him thunderously, with booming salvos of
cannon and the skies lighted up with huge gas fixtures.

The part that Dom Pedro was to play in the display
of the telephone was the most exciting story that Graham Bell carried back to Brantford for the benefit of his
family.

2

The Exhibition grounds lay along the banks of the Schuylkill River and filled all of the downtown part of Fairmount Park, 450 acres in all. There were two hundred buildings, with practically all nations represented. So extensive was the territory for conscientious visitors to cover that it became necessary to construct a miniature railroad of six miles to carry them about the grounds in handsome palace coaches. There were two enormous bronze statues, one of Columbus and one of Moses. Inasmuch as the Exhibition was to mark the hundredth anniversary of the nation, one might have expected to see George Washington in towering metal. Instead visitors were greeted by the awe-inspiring spectacle of the Great Lawgiver of the Children of Israel standing in fifteen-foot grandeur over a pile of rocks from which cold water spouted for the benefit of thirsty sight-seers.

The game which Abner Doubleday had invented nearly forty years before and was then known as baseball seems to have been overlooked but a series of cricket matches had been arranged.

There was an electrical section, in which the advances in applied science were displayed; all, that is, but the Multiple Telegraph and the telephone of Alexander Graham Bell.

It was his own fault. It could be traced to what everyone save a native of Scotland would call a stubborn streak in young Mr. Bell. At first he had said that he did not want his models displayed while they were still far from perfect. Then he took refuge behind the fact that the time for making entries had expired. Finally, he pointed out that the annual examinations of his pupils would begin the day after his exhibits would be judged, and he could not be in both places. But Mabel Hubbard, to whom he was now formally engaged, had a mind of her own. There was much determined debate and shaking of heads and perhaps a little stamping of feet in the house on Brattle Street. But the lady won. It was so late when she did that the electrical section was filled and the telephone (certainly the most monumental exhibit in all of those two hundred buildings) had to be placed in the Massachusetts Educational Section.

Many years later, when the inventor of the telephone could afford to smile over the stubbornness of his youth, Mr. Bell said: "I was not much alive to commercial matters. So I went to Philadelphia, growling all the time at this interruption."

The judging had been set for Sunday, June 25, when the space would be free of noisy spectators. It was stiflingly hot and the young man from Scotland, who found such weather almost unbearable, stood in the aisle in the East Gallery beside the receiving set which Thomas Watson had arranged, with the transmitter on the other side of the building, mopping his brow in discomfort of body and mind. He could see that the judges,

a group of most distinguished men, including Dom
Pedro and the great Englishman Sir William Thomson
(who played a big part in the laying of the Atlantic
cable), were feeling as miserable as he was. They were
carrying their tall silk hats in their hands and were
vigorously applying silk handkerchiefs to their brows.

When they came far enough down the aisle for him
to hear what was being said, he realized that they were
going to stop before coming to his exhibit. They had
stood as much of the heat as they could for one day.
His heart sank, for he had to catch a train that night to
get back to Boston in time for the examinations. Mr.
Hubbard had gone already and had left a nephew,
William Hubbard, to take his place with Bell. William
Hubbard was not much versed in science and could
hardly be expected to present the telephone in a successful light the next day. The exhibit would attract little, if any, attention under these circumstances.

But the massive figure of the Brazilian monarch did
not come to a halt with the rest of the judges. He had
caught sight of the disconsolate Bell at the end of the
aisle and had recognized him. Some few weeks before,
he had visited Boston and had talked to the young Scot
about his methods of teaching the deaf and the dumb.
He walked on, holding out his hand.

"I think it is Mr. Bell," he said, in a voice which
reached the other judges. "This is a far distance from
your classes. How are the deaf-mutes of Boston?"

"They are very well," answered their absentee

157

teacher. Then he decided to do what he could to avert the disaster which loomed ahead for him. He informed the emperor that his exhibit was the next one and so would not be judged. It was necessary for him to leave the city that evening.

"Then," declared the democratic monarch, "we must have a look at it now."

He took the inventor's arm and walked briskly to where the humble little receiver stood at the end of a seemingly endless line of wire.

The other judges followed, without any hint of interest or pleasure in the prospect. But the will of a ruler, especially one of such overpowering personality as the blondbearded emperor of Brazil, was not to be gainsaid. The telephone would be inspected after all.

Bell changed places with Willie Hubbard in order to speak himself into the transmitter, on the far side of the room. His voice had never been more resonant as he began on Hamlet's Soliloquy.

"To be or not to be——" he began. And then he paused, for he could see in the distance that Dom Pedro was pressing the membrane receiver to his ear and stroking his beard at the same time with a puzzled air. Would a voice carry clearly over this long stretch of wire?

He continued with the Soliloquy, speaking the immortal words with all the emphasis and firmness of tone which the two earlier Alexanders had taught him. Then he reached a most appropriate line near the close,

> And enterprises of great pith and moment
> With this regard their currents turn awry.

He saw that Dom Pedro had straightened up. Had *the current turned awry?* Would this enterprise of great moment prove a failure after all?

It was unfortunate for Graham Bell that he was not close at hand when the mercurial monarch raised himself to his full height and looked about him with eyes which were startled, awed, but not incredulous.

"A voice was speaking in my ear!" he cried.

It was clear to all about him that Dom Pedro was the most astonished man on the North American continent at that moment. One report has it that he dropped the receiver, exclaiming, "My God, it talks!" So carried away was he by this experience that the other judges evinced a desire to test the strange instrument also. Willie Hubbard waved an arm to Graham Bell to go on with the transmitting. Bell continued to speak, sometimes returning to the Soliloquy, for he found the opening line a peculiarly fitting one. In everything he said, he took pains to enunciate with the greatest clarity. He could see that Sir William Thomson (who would win acclaim as Britain's leading scientist under the title of Lord Kelvin) had taken the receiver and was exhibiting as much surprise as the huge Dom Pedro. Others took a turn, including Professor Barker of the University of Pennsylvania and Elisha Gray, one of Bell's competitors for honors in the electrical field. Then the whole group began to hurry across the building to the side where Bell was standing beside the transmitter. Apparently they wanted to see just what kind of magic he was invoking to create such an effect. Dom Pedro was in the lead, the tails of his formal coat flapping behind him and his beard bristling with excitement.

The explanation that the inventor gave was clear and concise and all of them, with the possible exception of the emperor, were so well grounded in electrical laws that they could understand. They all had heard a voice whispering in their ears. Although the words spoken had not been loud, they were reasonably clear and understandable. One doubt lingered in their minds. Had the voice actually traveled through the wire or was it nothing more than a thread telegraph (it was sometimes called the Lovers Telegraph), a device which transmitted sound along a wire mechanically? Would Mr. Bell be good enough to allow them to remove the apparatus to another location, where they could set it up for themselves? He said, "Yes," but that he could not remain to superintend the removal, as he had to return to Boston at once. In his own mind he was quite disturbed, for he feared that the delicate mechanism might be thrown out of kilter by the touch of alien hands. The depth of his resolution can be measured by his willingness to jeopardize the success of the invention in order to fulfill his obligation to his pupils.

The removal was carried out in his absence and the result was the same. Words passed over the wire from transmitter to receiver and there was no doubt in the minds of any of the judges that the sounds they heard were produced by electricity. It was reported to the inventor, back in Boston and absorbed in the examinations, that Sir William Thomson was so excited that he and Lady Thomson kept changing places, one speaking and the other listening, both laughing like "a pair of delighted children."

In due course Alexander Graham Bell received the Centennial prize awards for both the Multiple Telegraph and the telephone.

3

Graham Bell always said that the success of this display at the Centennial Exhibition was a matter of the greatest luck. By this he was not referring exclusively to the part played by Dom Pedro. He had in mind also how well the sounds came over the wire. They had never before behaved so well.

During the previous year, somewhere about the end of June, after the happy accident that revealed to Bell that "a magneto-electric current would produce by itself sonorous effects at a receiving station," the inventor and his assiduous assistant Watson decided that the time was ripe for the next step. Watson at the transmitting end talked to Bell at the receiver. The latter heard nothing. They changed places and after a moment Watson came charging up the stairs (they were working on separate floors of the Williams plant) exclaiming, "I heard your voice very distinctly and could almost understand what you said."

To Bell, who had anticipated something much better, the result was unsatisfactory. Nevertheless, he went ahead with the preparation of specifications for a patent. He was convinced that the undulating current was behaving properly but that the membrane receiver was not yet perfect by any means. When it would begin to function after the order of the human ear, then the telephone would become a usable instrument.

No doubt this disappointing result weighed on his mind and was responsible for his refusal at first to exhibit at the Centennial. But in the City of Brotherly Love luck smiled upon him. The sounds which came over the wire and spoke in the ear of an emperor were sufficiently clear to convince all the judges that one of nature's greatest secrets had been uncovered.

Chapter Eleven

The Famous Neighbor

1

MENTION has been made of the Honorable George Brown and of Bow Park. This low-lying block of farm land was the largest in all Canada and its owner was perhaps the best known man in the province.

Bow Park lay two miles south of Tutelo Heights and was reached by a road which ran sixty feet or more above the river until it dipped down to attain water level. Here, on a peninsula of nearly a thousand acres, lay the famous farm which Mrs. Brown had purchased, seeing the need of a place of relaxation for her famous husband. They spent their summers there, raising high-bred shorthorn cattle.

George Brown had by this time withdrawn from active participation in politics but he still used his powerful and trenchant pen in the columns of his newspaper, the Toronto *Globe,* as a whiplash to keep the Liberal party true to its traditions.

He was a man of extremes, in character as well as in his political views; extremely tall, extremely sober of mien, extremely active, and extremely ambitious; and to cap it all, most extraordinarily able. His hair was red, his nose was long, his eyes were serious. The editorials he wrote in the *Globe* were so convincing that the Scottish settlers, who formed the backbone of the population of Ontario, refrained from making up their minds about anything until the thundering gallop of the infallible editor's prose could be heard on the subject. As a campaign orator he could perhaps have drowned out all three of the Brantford Thunders; for his voice, while it could be persuasive, could rise also to great heights.

As a young man, living at Alloa, where sea breezes blowing up the Forth combined with the winds from the mountainous Highlands to make men rugged, he became involved early in controversies. He was prominently concerned in the wholesale withdrawal from the established Presbyterian Church which resulted in the Free Kirk. He became the uncompromising leader of the Wee Frees in Canada when he accompanied his father to that growing colony. Inevitably he became a prominent member of the Liberal party and raised his booming voice for reforms which have been accepted long since but were held in abeyance then: the fair division of the Clergy Reserves, representation by population, union with the western lands, and a national school system. His unwillingness to compromise when he became the leader of the party was largely responsible for the term "Clear Grits," which gradually was applied to all Liberals.

He established one curious record during his leadership, gaining power for the short time of two days only. It developed out of the selection of a capital city for the combined provinces of Upper and Lower Canada. The French-Canadian members wanted either Quebec or Montreal but Ontario had other ideas. In the end the selection had been left to the British Government and, acting on advice from the Colonial Office, the Queen decided on a small lumbering town on the Ontario side of the Ottawa River. A bitter discussion followed in the Canadian Parliament and a vote was taken which went against the government of Sir John A. Macdonald by the narrow margin of fourteen. Brown, exhilarated by the prospect of getting into power, rose to his feet and moved an adjournment on the grounds that the vote constituted an expression of lack of confidence. Macdonald, that wiliest of political tacticians, sent in his resignation that night and next morning crossed jauntily to the other side, where he took a seat in the Opposition benches. The easy smile on the face of the experienced Macdonald should have warned Brown of breakers ahead. Macdonald knew that the Liberals could not carry on with a meager majority supplied by the unpredictable Quebec bloc and that, if he asked for an appeal to the country, Governor Head would refuse to issue the writs. For two days the unyielding Scot battled to hold his tatterdemalion majority together while demanding of the implacable Head a fresh election. On the second day the French-Canadian bloc dropped away and a majority of forty was registered against the eager Brown, bringing his brief dream of glory to a sorry end. Not even in France, where new governments blossom overnight and fade away in rapid decline has so quick a change as this been known.

The trap laid for his feet by the clever Macdonald took some of the ardor out of the indomitable Scot and he fell into a condition of disgruntlement, when he would belabor in the columns of the *Globe* the party which he still led. Principles always were first with him, however, and he laid aside the personal vendetta when the question of confederation came to the front, being willing to ally himself with the suave "John A." in the effort to unite all Canada under one government. When the fight was won, he even consented to act as a member of the first federal government. He soon found that he and his leader could not work together and so handed in his resignation. In 1873 he was offered a seat in the Canadian Senate and accepted the post, continuing in that capacity for the balance of his life.

The Brown fortunes must have been considerable, for Bow Park was conducted with a lavish hand. The farm buildings, and the yards attached to them, covered nearly seven acres and included a great barn with a wing packed with power engines and a boiler for the preparation of winter food. There was a calving house where each cow and her calf had a box stall all to themselves. The highborn shorthorns, in fact, lived under conditions rather more comfortable than might have been found in the poorhouses throughout the province.

That the once indomitable leader of the Liberals had gone into farming with the same enthusiasm he gave to politics was evidenced once when he greeted a visitor with a gleam of triumph in his usually cool and reserved eye and an announcement that "the Empress of China has given birth to an heir." Later he explained that the Empress belonged in the top-ranking hierarchy of shorthorns and that it was a matter for much jubilation that both mother and son were doing well.

2

It was to this man of intense purpose that Graham Bell took his troubles. He needed money to carry on his experiments. The result of their talk was summarized by Mr. Bell in the evidence he gave in 1887 in suits entered for the canceling of the Bell patents; a legal move which resulted in a complete victory for the Bell interests.

I must direct attention [said the inventor] to my pecuniary condition in the summer of 1875, when I went to the home of my parents in Canada to recruit my health. During the year 1875 I had devoted my time to my electrical researches, to the neglect of the professional work upon which I was dependent for support. My associates, Mr. Sanders and Mr. Hubbard, although they had agreed to pay the expenses of the construction of my experimental apparatus, had made no provision to pay me for my time. When my professional work [the classes he maintained] had become disorganized, I could of course have made arrangements for my support with Messrs. Sanders and Hubbard; but on account of the delicate relations that began to arise between myself and Mr. Hubbard, I was unwilling to ask for any assistance. The delicate relations to which I allude will be understood when I say that Mr. Hubbard's daughter is now my wife. At the time I left for Canada in the summer of 1875 my health had given out, and my professional work also, and during that summer vacation it became a matter for serious consideration what I should do in the future. I desired to place myself in such a position that I should be able to marry. On the one hand I knew that if I devoted myself to my professional work, it was capable of yielding me an income; and, on the other hand, I believed that if I devoted my attention exclusively to my electrical inventions, they would bring me in a fortune.

George Brown listened intently while the youthful inventor made a similar explanation of his need for funds. It seems certain from what developed later that he did not feel too sympathetic to the plea. He knew, of

course, what young Bell was trying to do but he undoubtedly shared, in part at least, the opinion of most
people, that the telephone would never be anything but
a toy. No man who tossed money about as he did in the
improvement of his herds could be called closefisted;
and so it could not have been parsimony which limited
his interest. More likely he did not think it would be
either wise or dignified to be concerned with a scheme
which might be considered crackbrained. Perhaps the
way he had been tricked by John A. Macdonald into
the rash course which ruined forever his chance to head
a stable government had left its mark. Ever since that
humiliating occurrence he had looked at all proposi-
tions with a deliberate eye.

How much would be needed?

Not a great deal, explained the young inventor. No
more than enough to enable him to finish his experiments with a free mind. Perhaps at this point the figure
was mentioned which later was to have been embodied
in an agreement. The amount stipulated was twenty-
five dollars a month from the Honorable George Brown
and a similar payment from his brother for a period of
six months. For this, the Browns would be given a
half interest in the British Empire patents, including
Canada. Never before, surely, could an investment of
so little have produced so much in return!

It seems, nevertheless, that an understanding was
reached by which Mr. Brown and his brother, Gordon
Brown, agreed to make monthly payments to cover his

personal expenses. This was in September 1875 but after Bell returned to Boston the expected remittances were not received, nor did the promised agreement reach him. In his evidence the inventor stated further that the understanding had covered the taking out of patents in foreign countries by the brothers Brown. No application was to be filed in the United States Patent Office until the European arrangements had been completed.

George Brown sailed to England on January 25 of the following year. Graham Bell and his backers and associates waited anxiously for word of the filing in London. Nothing came. They were prepared to act immediately. The American application was sworn to in Boston and was sent to the solicitors in Washington, with instructions to act immediately when the word from abroad had been received.

On the witness stand the inventor explained the sequel in these words:

> Mr. Brown neglected to take any action in the matter and sent no cablegram; and Mr. Hubbard, becoming impatient at the delay, privately instructed my solicitors to file the specification in the American Patent Office, and on the fourteenth day of February, 1876, it was so filed without my knowledge or consent.

It was a good thing that Mr. Hubbard took it on himself to act. The application was filed in Washington on the morning of February 14. During the afternoon of the same day Elisha Gray filed his caveat, which described the idea he intended to employ in making a telephone!

The Honorable George Brown was not the only outstanding man who failed to see the potentialities of the telephone. Samuel L. Clemens, known to the world as Mark Twain, was given a chance to invest in it and declined. With the great humorist it was a case of many times bitten, finally shy.

3

Graham Bell was always hard-pressed for funds. In this connection I was told a story when I paid a visit to Brantford late in the autumn of 1958. My purpose was to listen to such faint echoes of the Great Event as the oldest residents of the city might be able to supply.

In the very early days there had been a log cabin on the point of land where Brant Avenue joined with Colborne Street, which was then, as now, the main commercial thoroughfare. One of the city's most colorful residents had erected a tavern on the site when the Bell family arrived. This was James P. Excell, about whom many stories are still told. In front of the tavern he kept a shop for the repair of umbrellas, the making of keys, and kindred activities and here he did all the work himself, wearing a black skullcap and treating everyone with the utmost kindness. The repair shop was, obviously, a way of keeping busy, for his profits came from the tavern. Apparently he did very well with it, for "Jimmy" Excell was a wealthy man by the time the Bell phaeton drove past his unique establishment on their first trip to the Heights. He had put out a sign above the entrance to the tavern which bore the lines:

This sign hangs high
And bothers none.
Refresh and pay,
And travel on.

This, no doubt, elicited an appreciative smile from the newcomers. Later they came to know the proprietor very well and to appreciate his unusual character. The skull-cap was for use only in the repair shop. When he went out, he invariably wore a high silk hat. He was later elected an alderman and proved in that capacity, it is said, both shrewd and farsighted.

This, of course, was before the automobile was anything more than a Jules Verne dream, and the best thing that had been evolved in the way of a bicycle was one called the Spider. The front wheel of this contraption was over three feet high and so the rider sat well up in the air and looked somewhat absurd as well as uncomfortable. Just about this time the term "boneshaker" was applied to the machine, which explains why few citizens of Brantford, or of any other community for that matter, were prone to use it. Because of this lack of facilities for personal transportation, a group of substantial citizens who lived along the Mount Pleasant

Road were in the habit of walking in each morning to the city, where they were all employed. Some of them came from as far out as Tutelo Heights and Melville Bell occasionally joined them. It was a jaunt of between two and three miles and the worthy citizens would arrive in a decidedly thirsty condition. And there, as though planted especially for their relief, was the thoroughly respectable Excell tavern with its familiar sign swinging lightly in the breeze. It became a habit to drop in for a glass of beer, which was quite long and cost at the time five cents. Or was it three?

The proprietor made a habit of smiling at them through the door into his queer little shop.

"Good morning, gentlemen," he would say. "I am glad to welcome you. But, if you please. One drink only each. You have your day's work ahead of you."

And now for the story. One day late in the year 1875 young Aleck Bell paid a call at the repair shop.

He found the proprietor hard at work, surrounded by such an assortment of ancient and modern umbrellas as could be found in no other establishment, perhaps, in the whole wide world. Old Jimmy being a wonder at putting recalcitrant timepieces back on schedule, there were clocks of all kinds in dusty confusion, waiting for his attention, seven-day clocks, grandfather clocks, grandmother clocks, decrepit old Act-of-Parliament clocks, their warped wooden panels showing dim scenes of Restoration bucks and dairy maids, cheap little clocks turned out by local makers. Racks were filled with bags and valises and satchels of all kinds, some for sale secondhand, some left hopefully for the touch of his skilled hand. The space in that fairy-tale shop was limited, so that queer articles stuck out unexpectedly from bins or hung from the ceiling or cluttered the windows. A strictly Dickensian place, where Jimmy Excell kept himself busy in his own cheerful way and from which by some kind of systemless magic the multifold articles left for him to mend finally emerged. Often, as good as new.

The proprietor gave his caller a friendly nod, noticing that young Mr. Bell seemed nervous. The latter stammered and his Adam's apple, no doubt, gave a twitch.

"Yes, my boy?"

"Mr. Excell, I need money. I need it rather badly."

Jimmy Excell, who heard everything that went on in town, knew about the son of the Bell family and his experiments.

"It is for the invention?"

"Yes, Mr. Excell. I have passed the—the experimental stage. It works. It will be a success. But there is still so much to be done. Improvements, you know, and materials and the cost of patents. And that takes more money than I have."

"How much do you need?"

The dedicated youth swallowed with increased nervousness. It was a colossal sum he must ask.

"Yes, my boy?"

"Three hundred dollars."

The mender of umbrellas laid down whatever task he had in hand and gave his visitor the benefit of a thoughtful stare. Then he left the room and his steps could be heard climbing the stairs which led to his living quarters above. When he returned, he carried a leather bag, tied carefully with a thick cord. This he opened and then shook out on the counter ten-dollar bills, gold pieces, silver. He counted out three hundred dollars, which made a formidable mound.

"There you are, my boy."

Alexander Graham Bell was at first too much taken by surprise to say anything. Then he stammered, "You will have a note for me to sign?"

The elderly man shook his head. "Young man," he said, "if your word is not good, then your signature will not be of value. I do not want a note."

This is the story repeated by some of the oldest residents. They had heard it, they said, from members of earlier generations. It is not included in what may be called the recognized stories of the Great Event. But it is such a pleasant anecdote that I cannot resist telling it here. And, from all the things I heard about that curious old man in the days when I was young and he could still be seen through the window of his fantastic little shop, I am sure it is exactly the kind of thing he would have done.

The question of financing the invention was always a difficult one for the two Bells, and many citizens of Brantford and Paris (after the successful long-distance test) were invited to participate. I doubt if much, or any, help was gained in that way. In my recent search along the trail which led to the telephone, I encountered many people in both places who spoke wistfully of what might have been. "Oh, if Great-grandfather So-and-so," they would say, "had not been *so* careful about his investments and *so* tight with his money, I would be a millionaire today." The financial arrangements made later in Boston took care of the problem but, before that, the inventor suffered an urgent need for funds. It seems just possible that the kindly tavern keeper may have come to his assistance in some such manner as the story suggests. Of course, when information is sought at second and third hand, it comes sometimes in the form of the confession of Tomlinson in Kipling's poem of that title, "Oh, this I have felt and this I have guessed and this I have heard men say."

I have tried to do as little guessing as possible and to label it always as such.

Chapter Twelve

The First Great Test

1

ALEXANDER GRAHAM BELL arrived in Brantford near the end of July 1876. This was later than usual but there had been many things to cause the delay; the nerve-racking days which preceded the application for a patent and the grim moments of waiting until it was granted, the exhibit at the Centennial, the unceasing probe by the inventor and his eager aide Watson in the hope of improving the instrument. There was also a matter of personal concern which, perhaps, outweighed everything else. Bell's engagement to Mabel Hubbard was official. Mrs. Hubbard had gone over completely to the side of the very much enamored couple and they were to be married the following year; or so they hoped.

Much of what he had been through could not be lightly dismissed. There had been the need to prepare the final copy of the patent application which he had begun in Brantford the previous year. It had seemed a perfect presentation of the case when he penned the last line at Tutelo Heights but through the early stages of the new year he had begun to realize a lack in it. Long days and longer nights had been spent in reviewing the detailed and technical copy but always he was conscious of something missing without being able to put his finger on it. Late one night, which he was spending at the home of his fiancée, he had sensed what was wrong. A few hours of concentration would do it. But Mabel insisted that he needed rest and must give up the dogged search for this one night at least. He pleaded his case so earnestly that, finally, she relented. The work was continued far into the small hours, resulting in the end in a discovery of what had been missing. A clause was needed to cover his theory of variable resistance. Once this ray of light came to him, he knew he had the solution. Before he retired, he had prepared a careful statement of the theory. On the basis of this, his patent had been granted on March 3 of that year.

The victory at Philadelphia, and the enthusiasm which grew out of the excited reception of the invention by Dom Pedro and Sir William Thomson, had begun to dim. There had been a noticeable check when an effort was made to transmit speech over long distances. As Mr. Bell expressed it himself in his speech at the Telephone Pioneers Convention in 1911: "On July 7, 9, and 22, 1876, attempts were made to use the telephone upon various circuits from Boston to New York, from Boston to Rye Beach and other places, but, unfortunately, with poor success. We did not get any vocal sounds on these circuits, although with two instruments, one in one room and another in another room in the Equitable Building and a circuit to Rye Beach, we did get some audible effect." It was here that one complete and clear sentence was spoken on the line and received at the other end.

If he could speak thirty-five years later of the "poor success" of these efforts, how poignant must have been his disappointment at the time! It was on the heels of this disillusioning experience that he came to Brantford. Some of this temporary regret was in his voice as he called a greeting to his parents, but there was in him a greater determination than ever to conquer the obstacles (he resolutely considered them minor) which still stood in his path. He was certain that in the undulating current he had the answer to the transference of sound by electricity, although much was still to be learned in the matter of manipulation and control. He must have been conscious also of a need to improve further the membrane telephone, and it was fitting and proper for him to bring that problem with him to Brantford, where the theory of the ear had been born.

Here is Bell's own report of what immediately preceded his return to Tutelo Heights: "I prepared a whole lot of apparatus, telephone coils of different kinds, high resistance coils and low resistance coils, long coils and short coils. And I carried these with me to Brantford." It should be added that he brought with him two membrane telephones and an iron-box receiver which he had used in the long-distance experiments out of Boston.

What transpired in the interval between his arrival in Brantford in the last week of July and the first of the three historic tests, which occurred on August 3, has not been put on record, unfortunately, in full detail. How helpful it would have been if the young inventor had decided to keep a report of everything he did or if his father had become a full-fledged Boswell for that important period! The notes the latter left are to the point but too brief to be of much real value.

We must be content, therefore, with the few hints of activity which are available. Graham Bell decided, quite wisely, to do some preliminary testing at home. Although his plan was to communicate messages over a wire from the house to the barn, he realized that a single wire, tautly strung, between the two points would not suffice. Accordingly he went to his friend and helper Thomas Cowherd. The latter had just completed the latest model of a telephone on minute instructions from the inventor, a rather extraordinary piece of equipment with three mouthpieces, by means of which three people would be able to listen in or to speak at the same time. It was decided between them that stovepipe wire would serve for the experiments but that a very large supply would be needed, perhaps every foot available in the city. Cowherd took on himself the task of cornering the supply. He was so successful that he drove out to Tutelo

Heights almost immediately thereafter with a wagon-load.

Graham Bell proceeded to set up the instruments of transmission in the house, attached to seemingly endless yards of stovepipe wire. With the unconcern of a true scientist, who loses sight of everything in the pursuit of his objective, he decided to take up the slack between point and point by winding the wire around the newel post at the foot of the stairs. Either his mother was unaware of what he was about or was the most patient of parents; at any rate, there was no protest when he proceeded to gouge spirals out of the wood in which he could wind and rewind the wire before carrying the line out through one of the windows.

Years later the need arose for some repair work in the interior of the house and an overzealous carpenter carefully filled in the grooves spiraling up the post. Today a few scratches only remain to show the use to which it was put at this important stage of things.

There were daily tests from that time on, with guests present during the evenings, in addition to those whose voices made them useful in the transmission of messages. The guests went back and forth between house and barn. The doors of the barn were kept closed to shut out all sounds from the house and in the evenings light was supplied there by lanterns suspended from the rafters. Most of the space remained in darkness, however. The receiver was set up on a tool bench and connected with the wires through a window in the gable. The tall young inventor preferred to remain at the receiving end, where he could check the results, giving each guest a chance to listen at intervals to the songs and recitals which reached them over this flimsy chord of metal. Perhaps the head of the gray horse could be seen, watching from a stall in the shadows.

Why has no artist thought of painting this historic scene?

The results obtained during these days of experimentation must have been encouraging. At any rate, Graham Bell decided on a bold course. He would try again to achieve a satisfactory transmission of the human voice over long-distance wires.

In the recording of what occurred during those memorable days in August 1876, we emerge completely from the realm of speculation. The story becomes clear, convincing, and complete.

2

The village of Mount Pleasant, which lay about two miles farther along from the point where the Tutelo Heights Road split off from the main highway, was a community which had been well named. The earliest settlers were probably traders and government officials, appointed to carry out whatever control and direction was needed in the Six Nations tract. They seem to have established themselves on a sound basis instead of being content with the makeshift existence of a frontier post. At any rate, Mount Pleasant soon grew into a community of substantial and handsome buildings. There was a spaciousness of high red-brick walls about the place and more than a hint of comfort and even elegance. There was from the beginning a sense of civic importance.

The ground on which the village stood had been included in the land grant to the Six Nations after the American War of Independence. Chief Joseph Brant had recognized from the beginning the need of white settlers as neighbors in order to show his red warriors how to work the land to advantage. The need was also felt of setting up a fund which would yield substantial annual payments to the tribesmen. He planned to sell off a large part of the land which was useless for hunting. But the Six Nations, under the terms of the treaty, had only the right of possession and did not hold any of the tract in fee simple. The best they could do was to lease the land to the whites for long terms. Chief Brant was not one to haggle and he agreed to give leases for 999 years. It was on this basis that the site of Mount Pleasant had been taken over. When the term expires, somewhere near the year 2700, the surviving descendants of Joseph Brant and his warriors may have a great heritage to share.

Mount Pleasant was established before Brantford

and so there was some reason for its tradition of superiority, a faint trace of which can be detected even today. This feeling was quite marked at the start, as witness the suggestion made at a meeting held to decide on a name for the new community which was being started at the ford which Brant had used on his first crossing of the Grand. A Mount Pleasantite named Biggar had held land at this point and had been helpful in improving the facilities for crossing. He was the first to come forward with a name. "I propose Biggarstown," he said. No enthusiasm was displayed for this suggestion and finally the name of Brantford was decided upon.

It was soon apparent that the new settlement on the Grand River was growing at a rate which would leave the older village very much in the shade. Streets were laid out, stores sprang up, brick churches and hotels were erected. Straddling the Grand at a strategic point, Brantford began at once to take on all the briskness of a growing town. Up on the plateau above the river, Mount Pleasant was firmly established in its own comfortable way and had no prospect of rapid growth. In fact, it was not long before some of its prominent families moved down into Brantford because of the greater advantages offered. The red-brick village refused to be disturbed. Those who were left said to themselves, "It is clear they need our help down there."

Mount Pleasant was probably at its peak in the days when the telephone was invented. Most of the houses were set in spacious grounds with plenty of trees around them. Roads to the west connected with the towns which were flourishing there. The Old Long Point Road ran directly south from the village to Lake Erie. The people had proved themselves to be of solid stock. Many of them had acquired considerable property and lived in comfort, and some of their young men had moved ahead in professional fields. Most prominent among the latter was Arthur Sturgis Hardy, who had moved into Brantford to practice law. He was already high up in provincial politics and would in time become leader of the Liberal party and premier of Ontario. In Brantford he was called Little Thunder. Mount Pleasant did not seem to resent the locale of his success. "It takes a Mount Pleasant boy," they said among themselves, "to show them his heels."

It also takes people of stout character to create legends. The village had many. There was, for instance, Fiddler Anne, who kept an inn in the heart of the village. No one seemed to know where she came from. She was a striking looking woman, who won her name by playing the fiddle for her customers. The villagers, save those who patronized her bar (all male, of course), saw nothing of her except on occasions when she went out for drives. She had a team of gray horses and she would race them through the community at top speed, their manes tossing with excitement. Sitting up alone in a high buggy and never looking to right or left, she perhaps conceived of this as a way of expressing contempt for the wives of the village.

Fiddler Anne had died years before and the site of her small inn was occupied by one of the best residences in the place. But in retrospect she had become a civic asset. Her memory was kept green and visitors were always shown the spot where her inn had stood.

Across the road from All Saint's Church, at the foot of the hill, there was a store kept by Wallis Ellis. In addition to carrying a general line of goods, it served as the office of the Dominion Telegraph Company. Isabella, the daughter of the proprietor, was the operator, and on the morning of August 3 she was busier than she had ever been before in her life. She and young Mr. Bell were literally up to their ears in work with stovepipe wire when William Biggar (a descendant of the Biggar already mentioned) came in with his twelve-year-old son James. Young Jim, watching what was going on with wide-open eyes, became one of the best witnesses of this important stage in the telephone saga. "They had miles of stovepipe wire," he said with proper awe. "Yes, just plain stovepipe wire, the kind that carries the stovepipes, you know. They were strung up around the store in the craziest ways. Isabella and that young Mr. Bell seemed to want to connect all this wire with the telegraph outside the store."

Young Jim heard what the busy couple told his father

186

and his sense of wonder grew. That very evening people were going to talk over the telegraph wires all the way from the Dominion Telegraph Company offices in Brantford!

3

The oldest residents of Mount Pleasant (speaking strictly at second hand, of course) disagree as to the attendance at the store of Wallis Ellis on that momentous evening. Some say that few were present. Others contend that the Ellis store, a tall and narrow structure with one-story additions on each side, serving as warehouses, was filled to overflowing; that, in fact, men were sitting on the counters and that the young people had their choice of standing or of squatting cross-legged on the floor. The belles of Mount Pleasant (the village was always noted for its pretty girls) were all on hand and sitting in a group with such regard for Late Victorian conventions that none of them showed more than the tip of a toe. Isabella Ellis was there, of course; she had been taking music lessons in Brantford and walking the five miles to and fro daily. Dolly and Mattie McEwen were there, and "Tatie" Biggar and Lizzie Mussen. The young men of the place were, of course, in attendance also, the Biggar, Phelps, Townsend, Bryce, and Devlin boys. If there were any chairs available, the matrons of the village had them.

It had been decided to transmit from the Brantford

office of the telegraph company and to receive on an iron-box telephone in Mount Pleasant. Graham Bell, watch in hand, stood in front of the receiver and it was quite apparent that he was in a highly nervous state. This is readily understandable, for this was his first attempt to transmit over a long-distance wire since the far from successful efforts between Boston and New York. Would better results be obtained this time? Would the voices come through, distinct and clear? The evening's test would be a crucial one.

At the stipulated time he replaced the watch in his pocket and with a set face raised the receiver to his ear. The onlookers fell into a complete silence and every eye in the store was fixed on him. He listened intently.

Graham Bell's story is that he heard a voice, which he thought to be that of his uncle David, begin on Hamlet's Soliloquy, the magnificent lines which were used so often throughout the telephone saga; with the words "To be or not to be . . ." A look of intense relief took possession of the inventor's face.

The thought ran through his mind, "It is to be." Perhaps he spoke the words aloud but in the excitement of the moment he could not be sure.

The program from the city continued for some time, to give all of those present in the store a chance to hear with their own ears. There were recitations from members of the Bell family. A song was sung by William Whitaker, a tinsmith from West Brantford who had a clear baritone voice. A soloist from one of the city

churches, Miss Mary Nolan, also took part. She was a
blue-eyed Irish girl who sang contralto. In later years
she went to New York and became a rather well-known
soloist in a metropolitan church. But to none of those
who heard her sing during the successful years did her
voice give as much pleasure as on this all-important
evening to one anxious young Scot.

The people of Mount Pleasant took turns at listening.
This was risky, for in that early stage it was necessary to
concentrate in order to make out what was being said.
At first it would seem like a distant twittering of birds or
a scraping of fiddle strings. After a moment or so the
sounds would begin to draw together and become
words. If the receiver were held close to the ear, the
intonations of the voice would become apparent.

Some of the company in the Ellis store did not seem
to get results but most of them heard distinctly. The
girls were particularly quick about it. They would
listen to a song and almost with the first bar they would
call out delightedly, "Oh, dem Golden Slippers," or
whatever the title happened to be.

It is probable that Graham Bell was happier that evening and surer of his ultimate success than at any earlier
test of his electric "toy."

The people of Mount Pleasant are still inclined to
think they have been somewhat overlooked in all the
speeches which have been made and in the stories which
have poured forth from newspaper presses. "It was

here," they say, "that the first really successful test was made. Why all this talk about Brantford and Paris and Boston and this neglect of Mount Pleasant?"

It must be conceded that they have a point.*

---

* I am glad to report that a commemorative plaque will be placed in 1960 near the site where this first successful one-way test was conducted over a real telegraph wire. This will be done by the Telephone Pioneers of Ontario and Quebec.

Chapter Thirteen

The Second Great Test

1

ALEXANDER GRAHAM BELL had made his plans with a degree of foresight seldom found in one so young and so harassed with detail. What he was aiming at was a test to be conducted between the homestead and Brantford on the evening of August 4, on which date his parents had arranged a reception in honor of an uncle from the colony of Victoria, Australia, Mr. E. S. Symonds, a brother of Mrs. Bell. The company would include a score of the prominent men of the city and it would be a rare opportunity to give a demonstration of the telephone. But a failure could not be risked before such a group.

By the experiments conducted at the homestead, he had learned that stovepipe wire could be used effectively for the transmission of speech. The Mount

Pleasant test had taken an important step forward by showing that voices could be carried over long distances. He felt confident, therefore, that success could be anticipated with a second test for the benefit of the guests.

But this would necessitate connecting the house with the telegraph line between Brantford and Mount Pleasant by stringing stovepipe wires to the junction point, a matter of a mile or so. To accomplish this in the few hours left meant prodigious labor. It may be assumed that he had little sleep that night, his mind filled with the need for a quick success, and that he was up and staring out of his bedroom window as soon as the rising sun cast its first rays along the Hamilton Road and sent arrows of light into the slow summer current of the river. As he stood there he may possibly have examined his hands and wondered how they would stand the work he must accomplish with them. It has often been said that Graham Bell had little skill with tools. His were the hands of a musician. Would he still possess the full quota of fingers and thumbs after the labors which lay ahead of him, the long hours of hammering and nailing and slicing and measuring?

The breeze which reached him across the river was fitful and warm. It would be a hot day.

The task to which he applied himself would have been relatively easy if it had been possible to utilize the fences, hedges, tree trunks, and gateposts with the full co-operation of the neighbors. There are two versions of what happened on that eventful morning.

First there is the direct evidence of Mr. William Brooks, the only survivor today who can speak with firsthand knowledge. He lives on a tract of land adjoining the homestead and his memory fortunately is clear on many important points. His father was Thomas Brooks, who farmed the land closest to the Bell holdings and who had always been the most friendly of neighbors.

"My father and I," he says, "were up towards the road, working in the fields. One of the fields had been planted to barley and the crop was ready to be harvested. My father had decided to get the crop in that day.

"Well, along came our neighbor, young Mr. Bell, carrying a coil of wire. He said there was to be a test of the telephone that evening and he wanted to run a line out to the Mount Pleasant Road. Could he string it along our fences?

"That was quite a problem," went on Mr. Brooks. "It was his idea to string the wire right across our gateway, which would make it impossible to get in or out with our loads. Father wanted to oblige, because the two families had become very friendly. He thought it over and then told Mr. Bell he would have to wait until we could get our loads through. He promised we would all pitch in then and help him with the wire."

The other version was supplied by William Sloane before his death many years after. He will be recalled as the young lad from Yorkshire, partly dumb and totally deaf, who came to the Bell home during the first winter of their stay at Tutelo Heights. He was still with them and had been working side by side with the son of the family. His recollection is that they could not use the fences and trees for the reason that Mr. Brooks has advanced, that it would close the neighbors in. There was another reason, the dread which the people of that time had of electric wires. It was his contention, therefore, that they found it necessary to sink poles at regular intervals and to string the line above the level of a man's head. He worked with his employer at hewing out makeshift poles and sinking them in the ground along the route.*

Later they were joined by Thomas Cowherd, the tinsmith, and two members of the Brooks family, Thomas and his brother Richard. The Brooks son, William, could hardly have been old enough at that time to take a hand in such heavy labors.

This earnest party worked for long hours under a broiling sun at the task of getting the line up. It was probably the hottest day of the year. A neighbor watched the perspiring band from the shade of a leafy maple tree. He was wearing a boater himself (the only kind of straw hat known at the time) and a cool suit

* It may have been that Sloane was confusing this with a permanent line which was constructed the following year.

of clothes. After enjoying the spectacle of other men working so hard, he returned home and had the following comment to make: "Silliest piece of tomfoolery ever was. He's clean daft."

There is one hitherto unpublished story told in Brantford about the stringing of the wire between the Heights and Mount Pleasant. Graham Bell had found considerable difficulty in getting strong enough batteries to carry the current but, apparently, had solved the problem at the last moment. On that hot and busy afternoon, however, the young inventor made a further and most disturbing discovery, that the fence posts were damp and would short the circuit. Zinc insulators with wooden caps were the only solution. At this point the ever useful Thomas Cowherd stepped in. He knew exactly the type needed and had a supply in his shop. He would install them himself.

This he did, working ahead of the stringing squad all through that broiling hot afternoon.

2

This was in those good old days when "calorie" was a French word for measurements of heat and was not thought of when men and women plied knife and fork. It was a period of stout eaters and the term "prominent citizen" generally implied a double chin and a waistline which could be spanned only by a very substantial and long watch chain. Melville Bell had invited twenty-three prominent citizens of Brantford for dinner at Tutelo Heights on the evening of May 4 and it goes without saying that there were many courses and that full justice was done to all of them.

Young Graham Bell, tired from a day of frantic activities, had watched the guests come strolling up the path to the house, wearing Prince Albert coats with proper dignity and striped trousers which detracted from that effect (for the pressing of trousers would not be introduced for another five years or so), and no doubt had said to himself, "This is my chance. I must take advantage of it." The meal, however, was a protracted one. There were many toasts to be proposed and many speeches to be delivered; and this, moreover, was a stage in the affairs of man when there was no such thing as a short speech. It was late in the proceedings before any mention was made of what had happened in Mount Pleasant the evening before. The eager eyes of the son of the house lighted up immediately and he began to talk of the test. As Helen Keller was to write later in her book *Midstream*, "He was one of those exceptional mortals who can never be in a room two minutes before the whole talk converges in his direction." Modesty had compelled him to wait almost two hours, but once he started to speak, twenty-three pairs of eyes, filled with sudden interest, were turned in his direction.

The group included two members of parliament,

William Patterson in the dominion house and Arthur Sturgis Hardy in the provincial (Big and Little Thunder), the principal of the Ontario Institute for the Blind, two sheriffs, two bank managers, three doctors, three lawyers; a goodly company, men of alert sense and financial substance. They listened intently to what the young inventor had to say.

The heat of the day still lingered when the last word had been spoken, although a slight breeze was blowing down the river and stirring the leaves in the poplar trees. The guests ventured out for a turn in the garden. It was a clear evening (the *Expositor* report the following day spoke of "the moon rising at its full") but the trees kept the grounds in shadow with only the bluish light from the conservatory to provide any illumination. The tips of the guests' cigars were like fireflies weaving back and forth.

The attention of the gentlemen was drawn to the wire which stretched from a rear room of the house to the barn when one of them asked, "Is that the wire which will carry a human voice?"

The answer was in the affirmative. A strange use could be made of this wire, and all other wires, for that matter.

The signal had been received that they were ready at the other end, the offices of the telegraph company on the south side of Colborne Street, about four miles distant. Here the "talent," who had been selected to demonstrate their powers over the air, were gathered. The guests at the Heights repaired to the front porch, where they found the receiver ready for use. With their cigars drawing comfortably, the worthy citizens sank back into their chairs, and waited.

The first listener heard a clear and resonant voice declaim Hamlet's Advice to the Players and one of them nodded and announced to the company that David Bell was giving a recitation. The second pair heard the clear and high soprano voice of Lily Bell, daughter of David and, therefore, Graham's cousin. The third listened to a fine rendition of "I Need Thee Every Hour" and knew at once that it was Mrs. Brooks singing, for she had rendered the same hymn the previous Sunday at Farringdon Church. She was the young widow of William Brooks and lived in the neighborhood with her two-year-old son. Later she married Colonel Tisdale and moved to Brantford. The voices were coming through as distinctly as they had the previous evening in Mount Pleasant.

On finishing their turns the guests would wander out onto the lawn, now damp with dew, where they wandered about and talked in low tones. There was much shaking of heads and the voicing of such phrases as "I can't understand how it's done" and "But I heard every word. Or nearly all." Perhaps they discussed the future of this strange instrument and were somewhat dubious about it. The telephone was ingenious, certainly, but could it ever be used for commercial purposes?

Could it take the place of face-to-face conversation?

Each guest had at least one long turn at the receiver. The program continued to come over the miles of telegraph and the flimsy stovepipe wires with good volume and clarity. The shaking of heads continued but toward the end it may have been that a less skeptical note was to be detected in what was said.

The tall young inventor stood beside the instrument, and watched, and listened. The hours he had spent in stringing the line down the hot and dusty road had taken their toll. His broad brow, usually of an almost poetic whiteness, carried the reddish glow of exposure to the August sun. He was clearly very tired. But there was in his eyes, as the witnesses later attested, a gleam of satisfaction, even of triumph.

It was late before the company dispersed, departing with the churning of buggy wheels, in the direction of the Mount Pleasant Road. In his bedroom a tired but very happy Alexander Melville Bell wrote in his diary the cryptic lines already quoted: "Gentlemen's supper. 23 guests. Telephone to Brantford. A line was run along the fence for the occasion."

3

It has been remarked in earlier pages that the public did not respond quickly to the arrival on the world scene of the telephone with any great confidence in its usefulness. To cast ahead, Professor Bell, in the course of his address in 1911 before the Telephone Pioneers of America, had this to say:

I want to speak now of a very curious thing. In the case of new inventions we are generally led to believe that the public is ready to swallow anything but that grave scientific men are the most skeptical of all. I found just exactly the opposite to be true in the case of the telephone. The public generally and the business men were very slow to perceive any value in the telephone. The scientific world, on the other hand, took it up at once.

The Brantford newspapers were exceptions, of course. They kept up a fusillade of information for their readers about the progress of the experiments and, if they entertained any inner doubts, they were careful to keep them out of print. But even the local scribes could err on the side of conservatism. After this test between Tutelo Heights and the city of Brantford on August 4, 1876, the second of the three epochal events, the *Expositor* published a report of what happened but gave rather too much emphasis to the social aspects of the occasion. It led off with the guest of honor and proceeded to name sixteen of the most prominent guests. The heading was "An Evening on Tutelah Heights."

It was difficult to arouse any great degree of enthusiasm elsewhere. Newspaper editors seemingly lacked the imagination to see what the invention might mean to life and the human race. Consider, for instance, the issue of the Toronto *Globe* of August 11, 1876, the day after the third and most sensational of the tests, a description of which will follow. As there was no telephone system in existence to expedite the carrying of news, the *Globe* had nothing about the truly remarkable story which had "broken" the night before along the Grand River but there had been time for something about the earlier tests to seep into metropolitan notice. The *Globe* was the great political organ of Ontario, owned and edited by the Honorable George E. Brown. It was a daily of curious proportions and would look very strange today, because the pages were ten columns wide. The first page had three columns of want ads to the left and seven columns of news.

The first page had some brief cables from abroad, including a report from London that the break in the cable between Australia and Java had been repaired; a leading article on Turkish atrocities in Serbia; a somewhat pedestrian report of the day in the "Imperial Parliament" in London; the latest news, grouped, from Nova Scotia, New Brunswick, Quebec, Ottawa, and Hamilton; reports on the annual rifle meet near Pt. St. Charles, on the race meet at Saratoga, and on four cricket matches in Ontario; a dissertation on Oddfellowship.

Had the *Globe* neglected to get any news of what had happened such a few miles to the west? The greatest invention of the century surely could not go unnoticed in the greatest newspaper of the country!

Page three had a column headed "Canada," made up of a mishmash of events of no manner of consequence, none of them honored by a heading. Halfway down the page there was an item, four and a quarter inches long, which began:

> We are informed by the *Expositor* [so, the *Expositor* correspondent must share the praise or blame] that at a party at the residence of Professor A. Melville Bell, on Friday evening, a rare treat was afforded to the guests in the experimental explanations made by Prof. A. Graham Bell, of the new system of telephony invented lately by that gentleman. [A brief account follows of the test made.] The practical exemplification of the lately discovered system of telephony made by the professor afforded much pleasure and information to those present.

The above is not intended as a criticism of the stout old *Globe*, which is today a national daily in Canada of first importance. It is introduced rather as a proof of the caution with which anything in the nature of scientific advance was viewed in the press of the day. The telephone was the second of the great inventions of that amazing last half of the nineteenth century, the succession which began with the telegraph and continued later with the phonograph, the electric light, the automobile, the flying machine, and the motion picture. As one marvel followed another in rapid order, men became used to it, if not a little blasé, and the public attitude changed to one of open credulity. The telephone came a little too early to share in this friendly reception and the chorus of "Pish!" "Tush!" and "Nonsense" with which it was greeted was perhaps natural after the world had supped so long and so copiously on the stories of Jules Verne. What a chance was lost for some public figure or newspaper editor to come out boldly and say: "This miracle which God and a bearded young Scot hath wrought will in a very brief time change the whole temper of life and lead to other marvels almost as great!"

4

Because it was an exclusive Brantford gift to the chain of contributory events, there was always more emphasis laid in the city on the second test than on either of the others. Almost from the time that I was old enough to understand adult conversation, I heard much talk about that memorable evening of August 4. When Mrs. Tisdale drove about the city (in a dogcart, I think), people would say, "That's the lady who sang into the telephone the night it was invented." The Tisdale family had moved into the city and had a home on Nelson Street which was admired very much because it had a square brick tower in front and a large greenhouse at one side with colored glass.

When the modern bicycle, with its pneumatic tubes, came into general use, parties of young people would ride out to the Heights. Melville Bell had sold the property in 1881, making a very small profit, and had moved to Washington. There had been several changes of ownership since. As soon as I owned a bicycle of my own, I rode out to see the famous house where so much had happened. It was farther than I had expected and I was a little tired from the heat of the day and the steep incline of the road when I finally sighted the house, with the peaked veranda and the long windows, set far back in the trees. There was no mistaking it even though the conservatory had been removed by that time.

I seated myself on the opposite side of the road and studied the place intently. At first I was disappointed in it, for it seemed small and quaint and not impressive. After closer examination, however, I thought it exactly as it should have been. I felt that the spirit of Alexander Graham Bell lingered about, that it might still be possible to catch the low notes of his piano and even to find the stovepipe wires and the tin cans and the ear of the pig he had used. Watt's steam engine, I said to myself, could not have been invented in a kitchen which did not serve as living quarters for the family as well. I wondered if any great advance in science had been conceived in a mansion filled with silver and glass and velvet hangings and with footmen in every hall. I became convinced quickly that the Bell homestead provided the perfect setting for this remarkable story.

A man came out into the grounds and proceeded to do some clipping and pruning. He did not look once in my direction, so I assumed he had become accustomed to visitors who stood about and stared. I walked up and down the road and studied the place from every angle. Many odds and ends of the story had become lodged in my mind and they now aided me in identifying the most interesting points. The french door to the right of the front entrance was, clearly, the one he had used on his returns from Boston, shouting greetings to his parents. The small wing behind the spot where the conservatory had stood was his workroom. The bedroom window above had been his. The original paths through the grounds seemed to have been left unaltered and some, at least, of the outhouses were still standing.

As I pedaled down the road on my return trip, my mind was filled with one thought, the youthfulness of the inventor. This young man, alight with the spark of genius, was in his early twenties when he arrived in Brantford. The idea of the telephone was firmly fixed in his mind even then and it took a few years only to complete the invention. Never before had so young a man accomplished such a miracle!

I had intended to ask permission to go back into the grounds and inspect the sofa seat, for there the great inspiration had flooded the imaginative mind of the inventor. But I had many things to do and so I contented myself as I rode away with watching over my shoulder the roof of the curious little house until it disappeared from view.

Chapter Fourteen

A Word about the Man

1

THE story of the invention is drawing to a close and it seems proper to pause at this point and tell something more about the man before proceeding to the final scene.

"Bell was a pure scientist," wrote Thomas Watson in *Exploring Life*. "Making money out of his idea never seemed to concern him particularly." Out of the volumes which have been written about him, this reference by his closest helper and mechanical man Friday does much to reveal his inner self. Graham Bell would never have given up his teaching (which he always regarded as his first responsibility and which he loved) if the prospect of making money or winning fame had been his chief incentive. It was the scientist in him which kept him working at his idea, experimenting, probing, laboring day and night with fanatical zeal. The financial re-

wards seemed to him so little important that he gave a
three-quarters interest in the telephone company set up
in Canada to his father and saw to it that all who had
helped him were suitably rewarded. He put into his
wife's hands the control of his financial affairs. On one
occasion, when the inevitable litigation over the validity
of his patents had come up for a hearing in the
courts, he happened to be in Canada. He threw up his
hands and declared that he was prepared to let the patents go and devote the rest of his life to the teaching of
underdeveloped children rather than become involved
in more legal entanglements. It required a great deal of
pressure to make him change his mind. But, when he
gave in and appeared in court, he proved such a convincing witness that the award was a sweeping victory.

All his life he seems to have yearned for the work he
understood best, the teaching of the deaf and dumb.
He may quite possibly have felt that what he did for
Helen Keller was as important as the flash of inspiration
which came to him on that summer day as he sat in the
ease and isolation of the sofa seat. In her book, written
many years after, Miss Keller spoke of the first time she
met him. "Child as I was," she says, "I at once felt the
tenderness and sympathy which endeared Dr. Bell to
so many hearts. . . . But I did not dream that that interview would be the door through which I should pass
from darkness into life, from isolation to friendship,
companionship, knowledge, love."

His modesty played a large part in winning so general

an affection. He had been well liked when he came to Tutelo Heights as an ailing young man. If at first his experiments were regarded with skepticism, everyone seemed willing to help him. After the third of the three tests, with which this narrative will be brought to an end, the world began to waken up to the importance of what he had done. The New York *Herald* said, "The effect is weird and almost supernatural." The Boston *Post* referred to the telephone as "one of the most remarkable inventions of the present age." It was becoming clear to men of open minds that a miracle had come to pass which would usher in a great new era.

But when "Sandy" Bell (as his wife preferred to call him) brought his bride to Brantford soon after their marriage in 1876, he had not changed a whit. He was still modest, cheerful, filled with high spirits. One of the neighbors, Miss Rebecca Wye, told of a reception which was held on the arrival of the newlyweds.

"We'll have a little dance," said the young man for whom the door of fame had swung open so wide.

He escorted his wife, who seemed to the neighbors most pretty and stylish (a word of highest praise then), to the center of the floor while Miss Wye went to the piano to play a waltz. For the benefit of his wife, he raised a finger in the air and marked the time, One—Two—Three! Although the bride could hear nothing, she kept step perfectly. The young husband explained this later to Miss Wye. "She can feel the musical vibrations through the soles of her feet," he whispered.

The neighbors on the Heights told of one incident with the greatest delight. "Aleck's mother," they said, "came out to greet them and broke an oatcake over her daughter-in-law's head! We found out later it was an old Scottish custom. It meant the bride would never go hungry in her husband's home."

It seems to have been effective in this case!

After the stage which marked the end of Brantford's participation in the saga of the telephone, there was much still to be done to improve the machine which conveyed the human voice so unerringly over miles of wire. It was a relatively simple matter, however, to make reciprocal connections, with an instrument that could be used as both transmitter or receiver. More difficulties cropped up in finding ways to make "central" connections. The inventor played his part in all these advance steps but his interest wavered as the years went on and the telephone became the most complicated of all devices serving a world-wide public. He became more and more willing to leave the continuous improvements and advances in the hands of the experts employed for the purpose.

I have never heard at what point he withdrew completely from the never ending research. Perhaps he was always consulted on important points. He made it clear, however, when he came to Brantford in 1906 and I interviewed him for the *Expositor,* that his interest had been transferred to newer things. He was deep in the

problems of flight and his luminous eyes lighted up as
he spoke of the possibilities he foresaw in the conquest
of the skies. This was another phase of the pure scientist
in him. When one task had been completed, he was not
content to rest on his oars; he turned to distant and
green fields.

2

Consider the accomplishments to his credit after his
work on the telephone had been completed:

He developed two new breeds of sheep;
He was co-inventor of the aileron;
He experimented with an X-ray device;
He invented the action comic strip;
He invented a system of air conditioning;
He invented an electrical probe for surgeons;
He invented the wax-disc phonograph record;
He suggested the iron lung;
He developed the fastest motor boat in the world for
its time;
He suggested an echo device for measuring the depth
of water;
He suggested the method of using radium in deep-
seated cancer;
He predicted air power would be the key to world
supremacy;
He suggested a sound detector for locating icebergs;

He invented a method of transmitting speech and sounds over a beam of light;

He invented a device to take husks from wheat before grinding;

He invented a method of changing sea water into drinking water.

It is clear that he spent the rest of his life in continuous activity and that his imaginative powers were never at rest.

3

The life of this truly great man offers endless variety and color for full biographical treatment. This is not a biography, nor is it a complete story of the invention (the invention of the telephone is still going on and probably will never end), but the temptation to introduce more stories about him, even in this brief treatment of the subject, cannot be resisted, particularly since the anecdotes selected deal exclusively with the life of the Bell family. They are concerned in large part with the phase of home life which children are prone to remember best, the gathering for meals.

Mrs. Grosvenor and Mrs. Fairchild, daughters of the inventor, like to speak of the true Scot coming out in their father at breakfast time; how he always had his porridge served in the approved Scottish style, the hot oatmeal in one bowl and chilled cream in the other. He would take a spoonful of the oatmeal and dip it in the cold cream. A magnificent dish, truly, for anyone who can disregard the matter of calories! Soft-boiled eggs, eaten out of the shell in the English fashion, was his only other breakfast dish.

Graham Bell was in no sense a gourmet and, in fact, he paid little attention to food. But he was very particular about how it was served. He liked to eat off clear white plates and even went to the extent of having a service made in France with no more design than a fine gold band and his A.G.B. monogram. At home he always drank liquids through a glass tube, as he wanted "to put the liquid into his mouth and not his mouth into the liquid." And, being law-abiding in the strictest sense, he allowed nothing of a spirituous nature on the table during the years that Prohibition was legally in force.

He had certain traits which are still affectionately recalled. It was his invariable rule to seat himself opposite his wife with the light on his face so he could indicate by lip movements the course that the conversation was taking. Thus she was never left out and could enter into the talk at will. The two daughters learned to assist their mother in the same way.

Another rule grew out of his dislike for gossip. He could not abide criticism of anyone, even those who richly deserved what might be said of them. If members of the family expressed an opinion which was unfavorable, he would sit very still for a moment or two. Then he would fold his napkin. If this danger signal were disregarded, he would push his chair back from the table.

"And that," attests Mrs. Fairchild, "always stopped us." An admirable rule, especially for one who had been the target for so much envy and bitterness in the courts and from rival scientists.

Perhaps the favorite family anecdote is of the time when their kindly but somewhat absent-minded parent went to a reception at the White House in garb which might be termed individualistic. He had been out for a drive with Mrs. Bell and, on returning to the house to get into formal attire, he noticed nothing but the swallow-tailed evening coat laid out on the bed. He donned his overcoat downstairs before Mrs. Bell joined him and, as she preceded him in the line, she did not have a chance to notice him until they returned to the home of a relative, Mrs. Keenan, for tea. Quite unaware of the sensation he had created earlier, and with the touch of the actor which was inherent in all the Bells, he came stalking through the portieres with a dramatic flourish of his arms. The temptation is heavy on me to build the story a little by saying that the bearded and jovial inventor was wearing his glossy evening coat over golfing plus fours. The truth is, however, that it was nothing worse than a pair of striped morning trousers.

Even at that, Mrs. Keenan had heard one colored doorman say to another, in openmouthed amazement, "You see dat?" To which the other replied, "Oh, he's Telephone Bell. He can dress any whichever way he please."

4

He seems to have been the most modest of men as well as the possessor of blithe spirits. When things pleased him he was very likely, even in his advanced years, to indulge in a furious Indian war dance or a Highland fling. He did not live long enough to hear people say, as many did: "Who invented the telephone? Why, it was Don Ameche, wasn't it?" How his stout frame would have shaken with laughter if he had! His leonine head was never held high with self-pride. Seldom has one who had accomplished so much demanded so little praise.

He remained a hard worker all his life; the volume of his labors increased by his insistence on seeing everything for himself, the lesson that the great English monk, Roger Bacon, taught so many centuries ago. Not content to accept textbook facts, he would have to demonstrate each step for himself. This involved him in much effort that was perhaps unnecessary but which always left him quite sure in his own mind.

It has been said that he was lucky; but it had been demonstrated long before that by working steadily and trying every method and device, the happenings which are called luck are brought about. By his continuous efforts, Alexander Graham Bell won for himself a series of lucky turns as beneficial as the proverbial good fortune of the Musgraves. There was, in the first place, the good effect of the family move to Tutelo Heights, the fact that the fathers of two pupils in Boston proved so believing and generous, the decision of his father-in-law which resulted in getting his specifications registered at the Patent Office a few hours ahead of a competitor. And finally there was to be the very lucky chance which revealed the presence in a waste basket of a most important letter.

All this helped. But, even if some things had not come about so fortunately, Alexander Graham Bell would have found other ways around the hidden corners.

Chapter Fifteen

The Third Great Test

1

THE third test was a necessity. The first two had been made over limited distances and with makeshift materials. Now the instrument must be tried for a longer distance and over regulation telegraph wires with batteries of sufficient power; the same conditions which had prevailed when he attempted to speak between Boston and New York.

Young Mr. Bell thought it over carefully and decided to have the test between Brantford and Paris. The latter town at the junction of the Grand and Nith rivers was a logical choice for two reasons. It was just under eight miles distant from Brantford and it had been the home of the Bell family for a short time when they first came to Canada. The Reverend Thomas Henderson, who had persuaded them to come, still lived there.

The inventor wrote to the headquarters of the Domin-

217

ion Telegraph Company on Front Street, Toronto, asking to rent a line for one hour between the two points at eight o'clock on the evening of August 10.

It so happened that the telegraph companies in Canada had been pestered by crackpots with all manner of wild schemes and impossible improvements. The official who received the letter grunted as he read it and consigned it to his waste basket. "Another of these cranks!" he undoubtedly said to himself.

Graham Bell, knowing that every hour counted, waited several days for an answer. None came. He was forced to the conclusion finally that the telegraph company had no intention of granting his request and, in fact, considered the matter of such small importance that an answer was not necessary. With the utmost reluctance, young Bell decided he must postpone all further experiments until his return to Boston.

But an assistant in the telegraphic offices happened to see what happened to the letter. This was Lewis B. McFarlane, a name destined to become one of first importance in the history of telephony in Canada. Perhaps it was just a lucky chance which led him to the letter in a search for something else. Whichever the reason, he retrieved the note and read it when he saw the signature of the sender. The contents interested him at once. Some faint echoes of what was happening in Brantford had already reached his ears. At any rate, he got in touch with W. H. Griffin, the manager of the company in Brantford. The latter had been helping Mr. Bell almost from the time that the experiments began and he had been useful in loaning various bits of apparatus and lengths of scrap wire. The local manager, in fact, was one of the relatively few who had seen the possibilities in the strange new instrument almost from the first. He made a most enthusiastic report on the project. As a result Mr. McFarlane either persuaded his superior to reverse his decision or took it on himself to act on his own authority. A letter was written to Alexander Graham Bell granting permission for the use of the line between the two points for the hour requested.

The reply was a last-minute reprieve for the inventor. There was barely enough time to get his materials together and to make all the necessary arrangements. His father, fearing that the permission would not be received, had made plans to be out of town that night and so could not be included in the program.

Once again the hand of Fate had intervened with no more than a few hours to spare.

Perhaps a brief interruption may be made at this point to say something about the young man who thus played the role of the god from a machine. The career of Lewis B. McFarlane had something of the Horatio Alger ring about it. Born in Montreal in 1851, he became a telegraph messenger at the age of fourteen. He was so enthusiastic about the possibilities he saw in telegraphy that he spent several years traveling about the United States, beginning at New Orleans and working north to

Detroit. In this way he obtained so much knowledge of the new trade that at the age of twenty-five he was appointed assistant to the general manager in Toronto, arriving there in time to intervene in the Bell matter.

It may have been that the initiative he showed on that occasion led to his recognition later. The Dominion Telegraph Company decided to seek rights to the use of the telephone in Canada and sent young Mr. McFarlane to Brantford to negotiate a deal. On the occasion of his first visit, he found only Melville Bell and his brother David at the homestead. They gave him a most friendly reception, with songs, piano numbers, and recitations. The visitor was so pleased that he had barely enough time to catch the return train. A second visit was more fruitful and on February 8, 1879, an agreement was signed which granted rights to use the telephone in connection with telegraphic services. The following year a division was established to handle the telephonic rights and Lewis McFarlane was made head of it. In 1915 he became president of the Bell Telephone Company of Canada.

2

Alexander Graham Bell drove to Paris late in the afternoon of August 10, taking with him the special equipment he would need, which included the iron-box receiver made by Watson in Boston. Brantford was to do the sending of the messages, Paris the receiving.

It was a long drive and he had plenty of time for earnest reflection. He realized to the full the importance of this evening. His backers in Boston were, he had reason to know, more concerned still with the Multiple Telegraph than the telephone. If the night's test proved a failure, he might find it necessary to drop the telephone and devote his time again to the first invention. This he did not want to do.

The warm weather had persisted all week and the drive to Paris was an uncomfortable one. When he reached a point on the road from which the town could be seen, rising abruptly from the level of the river, a breeze was felt and he experienced an immediate sense of relief. The town seemed quiet, because the factories had closed and the employees had already gone home to supper. The residential streets wound upward around the hillside and in a few hours there would be innumerable beads of light glittering through the trees which covered the higher reaches.

When Graham Bell drove carefully over the Lower Town Bridge, he must have felt that he was visiting a deserted town. The bridge was empty, the business streets were bare, and the clop of his horse's hoofs was startlingly clear. Looking about him he perhaps wondered if any interest would be shown in what he proposed to do. It seemed possible that the weary townspeople would not brave another climb down from the heights to be on hand. But he did not need to speculate on that score, for a young man named Dunlop had seen to it that the whole town knew what was afoot.

George P. Dunlop was the Paris telegraph operator and, when Graham Bell arrived, he was alone in the office, which occupied part of the boot and shoe store of Robert White on Grand River Street. After hitching his horse in front of the store to a post of an overhead porch, the young inventor went in, his arms filled with the special equipment he had brought.

The two young men had met once before. They shook hands rather solemnly, as befitted such an important occasion, and Graham Bell asked the telegrapher if he knew of the arrangements for the evening. Dunlop knew all about them. He nodded his head with mounting animation and said that the word was all over town. It was early yet but plenty of the townspeople would be "down" to watch the test.

"They'll be here," he said. "Mayor Whitlaw and the rest of the big fellows." Did Mr. Bell know Bernard Travers, the Paris express agent for the Grand Trunk? Well, he would be down as soon as he had his supper. The people of Paris, he made clear, had been watching developments closely and were inclined to think there might be something in the telephone after all.

Having the store to themselves, the two young men set to work to adjust the equipment. Dunlop looked at the iron box and asked some questions about it. Then he put on a flat-topped and broad-brimmed hat of black felt and made for the door. He wanted to be certain that certain special friends of his would be "on the job" in time to watch. It was quite apparent that the yeast of excitement was rising in his veins.

The Reverend Thomas Henderson was the first to arrive. He was in a state of nervous tension, knowing to the full what depended on the result of the test. A chair was provided for him and he sat down close to the receiving apparatus. Outside, the postsupper quiet of Grand River Street was being broken by the clump of heavy heels and the sound of many voices. People were calling back and forth in the expectation of an exciting evening. Bell walked to a front window and looked out under the shingled veranda in front of the store.

He saw groups of men standing about, most of them wearing cloth caps and ascot ties. There were quite a number of girls, all of whom had escorts (propriety demanding that they never go out alone in the evening) and all of whom were well dressed. They wore bodices with tails in the back, in what was known as a "postilion" effect, or with the princess line, tight at the waist and extending over the skirt to form a peplum. Their straw hats were small, about the size of a dessert plate, and were worn well down on the forehead. Their shoes had rounded toes and there were rows of buttons in scallops on the sides. If Graham Bell had been able to spare a moment to observe these pleasant details, he would have thought the girls of Paris very pretty and trim indeed.

The door of the shop kept opening and shutting. The

"big fellows," promised by young Mr. Dunlop, were putting in an appearance and Mr. Henderson was introducing them in turn to the inventor. Mayor Whitlaw was among the first, and also the express agent, Bernard Travers. Several of the most important manufacturers of the town came in, including John Penman, the founder of the Penman mills, a large textile factory, Messrs. Clay and McCosh, who operated a woolen mill, Messrs. Brown and Allen, who owned another factory. Most of the merchants who had stores on the street were beginning to stroll over. Mr. White, the owner of the shoe store, was present, needless to state, looking slightly concerned as the company multiplied. By the time George Dunlop returned from his brief excursion to spread the tidings among friends, the street outside was as crowded as during the busiest of business hours. Very soon after, Dunlop bolted the front door, remarking that the shop would not hold any more.

The young inventor had to mop his brow frequently but it was not due entirely to the crowded condition of the shop. This was the first occasion on which he had found it necessary to operate before a large company made up almost entirely of strangers. He was obviously nervous and kept looking at his watch, like an amateur actor awaiting his cue in the wings.

"One minute to eight, Mr. Dunlop," he said, finally.

"We're ready." Dunlop had seated himself behind the corner counter with one hand on his telegraph key. His share in the proceedings would consist largely of communicating back and forth with W. H. Griffin in Brantford on a separate wire, about any adjustments which seemed necessary. He explained later that at the start he was disturbed as to whether the battery on the line would perform satisfactorily. It was located in Toronto, sixty-eight miles from Paris.

3

Bell took a quick look about the crowded store, his face tense with the anxiety he felt. "If only my father were here," he thought. Bell picked up the receiver. As the notes he wrote next day make clear, he suffered an unpleasant shock.

"The moment I put my receiving instrument to my ear, I heard perfectly deafening noises proceeding from the instrument, even when there was no battery on the circuit. Explosive sounds like the discharge of distant artillery were mixed with a continuous crackling noise of an indescribable character." He was not completely discouraged, however, for his notes continue: "In spite of this disturbing influence I could hear vocal sounds in a faraway sort of manner. The singing on the air was distinctly manifest."

Four words from *Macbeth* had been audible. Bell took his ear away from the receiver and looked at Dunlop, who was crouching behind his counter. The latter asked, "Trouble?"

Bell waited before answering. Three voices, two male

and one female, had begun to sing. The first stanza was recognizable as "The Maple Leaf Forever" but the interfering sounds made it impossible to distinguish the words.

"Please send this. 'Can hear faintly "Maple Leaf." Key of D. Words indistinguishable. Disturbance on line. Instruct operator there to change the electromagnet coils on their instrument from low resistance to high resistance.'"

When he had completed this same change in the receiving end, Graham Bell lifted the instrument to his ear with more than a hint of reluctance. He seemed afraid to face what the result might be. If the reception had not improved, what more could he do?

For a moment his expression did not change. Then his eyes seemed to light up. Still holding the receiver to his ear, he turned to Dunlop and nodded. The trouble had been in the use of low-resistance coils, as he had expected!

The next day he included in his notes, "The vocal sounds then came out clearly and strongly, and the crackling sounds were not nearly so annoying, though they still persisted."

David Bell, the inventor's uncle, resumed the program with lines from *Macbeth*. In a few moments he stopped and asked, "Do you hear me now?"

Bell waved excitedly to Dunlop. "Wire them, 'Yes, I hear you.'"

The program was resumed then with more songs. Bell

recognized all the airs and was quite certain that the singers were his uncle David, his cousin Lily, and Mr. Griffin. A few moments of silence followed while the inventor kept the receiver pressed to his ear. He seemed to sense that the climax of the evening was close at hand.

"To be or not to be," began a voice at the other end of the wire.

Bell gasped with surprise. It must be his father's voice. But that, he believed, was impossible. Melville Bell was not in Brantford.

He whispered excitedly to Dunlop. "Wire them, 'Change has improved transmission greatly. Whose voice did we hear speaking Hamlet's Soliloquy? Was it my father's? Important!'"

The message was ticked off immediately. There was a pause at the Brantford end. Then he heard again those familiar tones, clear, resonant, unhurried, each sound formulated perfectly.

"Yes, my son," said Melville Bell. "This is your father speaking."

The voice went on to explain that at the last moment he had found it impossible to tear himself away to keep his appointment in Hamilton. It had been postponed and he had joined the group in the telegraph office.

The excitement of the younger Bell can easily be imagined. If he had been in a position to indulge in any physical manifestations, he undoubtedly would have gone through the gyrations of the war dance of the Six Nations. This was the first perfect test. Every intonation of his father's voice had reached him over the wire. No longer was the telephone a myth, a dream, a "toy." It was a reality.

A long period of continued effort, he knew, stretched ahead still. The instrument must be adapted to allow of conversations over the wire and later to permit users to call any number of other subscribers. But these advances would come in time and without undue difficulty. What counted in this supreme moment was that he had been vindicated. It had been proved that the human voice could be transmitted over a wire for long distances.

From the moment that the familiar timbre of his father's speech reached his ear, the mind of Alexander Bell, for the first time perhaps, was freed from any shadow of doubt.

He wired an exultant message: "Father, your presence in Brantford at this time completes my joy to-night."

4

The citizens of Paris, who had turned out in such numbers to witness the test, deserved to have a share in the great moment. Graham Bell had his brisk helper send off another message, asking his father to continue talking until further notice. Then he called to the audience to take turns at the receiver. Needless to state, they were eager for the chance. One by one they came up and applied an ear to the iron-box receiver. Without exception, they recognized the dramatic tones of the great elocutionist declaiming Shakespeare eight miles away, each phrase as clear almost as though he were in the store with them. Skepticism took wings and vanished from that hot and crowded emporium. There was general excitement. History was being made in Paris, and they, prominent men in their own bailiwick, were having a share in it.

They nodded to each other and smiled. Hands reached out to thump silently the shoulders of neighbors. Without a sound to interfere with the reception, they lined up to shake the hand of the obviously weary young man who had brought this miracle to pass.

The people in the street had been waiting impatiently for word from inside. What was happening? Was the test proving successful or did the lack of an announcement mean that nothing was being received over the telegraph wire?

There was general delight when word of the results finally reached them.

"It works! It works!" cried an excited spectator.

Someone near the door held up a hand to admonish the crowd. "Easy now! Not so much noise. People in Brantford are talking to them in there. And singing. It can be heard as plain as day."

Some of the privileged witnesses stepped out for

a breath of air and eager volunteers from the street took their places inside in the hope of having a turn at the receiver. Too affected to speak, Graham Bell left the handling of the instruments to Dunlop and began to pace up and down in the limited space of the store aisle. For a few minutes he did not hear what was going on around him, his mind being filled with one thought. The last high hurdle had been cleared!

Melville Bell stopped transmitting and others at the Brantford end took his place. Songs were sung, both sacred and profane. The reception was now so good that the songs were recognized almost with the first bar. The listeners would shout out the titles. "Oh, Wouldn't You Like to Know?" "The Little Round Hat," "Charming Judy Dockerty." Dunlop wired the title back each time and this raised the spirits of the Brantford group to such a pitch that they began to shout congratulatory messages. Staccato asides were hurled back and forth between the two stations. The singers began to indulge in parodies. Just what these were is not on record but perhaps they sang "D'ye Ken Aleck Bell?" "Listen to the Telephone," and "Ding-dong, Ding-dong, Bell."

Only once was the Paris audience stumped. In the notes he set down the next day, the inventor referred to their inability to guess a popular song of the day called "Maggie May." It was Griffin who sang this one, with other voices joining in the chorus.

The wire had been leased for one hour only but nine o'clock came and went unnoticed. The avid listeners in

Paris kept demanding another turn at the receiver. The keys under the nimble fingers of Dunlop kept on ticking out requests for more songs. The group in Brantford sang until their throats were husky and the stream of recitation ran on until they could think of nothing more to declaim. The floor of the store was white with copies of the messages which Dunlop had wired to the city.

It was not until eleven o'clock that the demand for more ceased and the witnesses began to leave the store in voluble groups. Robert White, the proprietor, closed and locked the front door. This great episode in the history of the town had come to an end.

Incidentally, the telegraph company never presented a bill for the use of the wires. This generous gesture compensated for the anxious days while Graham Bell was waiting for their answer to his letter.

The spectators, surfeited at last with this unfolding of a new wonder, began to divide and start for home in various directions. As they ascended the wooden sidewalks to the hill regions, where their cobblestone houses were so picturesquely set back in clumps of trees, they talked about what they had observed. Their voices came down clearly to the few who still stood about in the vicinity of the shoe store and it was evident that they had been jolted into new lines of thought.

Bell was the last to leave. He had shaken hundreds of hands in farewell, or so it seemed, and he was so tired that he carried his equipment to the buggy with slow steps and bent back. The ever kind Mr. Henderson had wanted him to spend the night in Paris but he had refused the invitation. He must have what was left of these precious hours with his own family. He was eager to hear everything that had happened at the Brantford end and what had been said. They would sit down together in a circle and talk far into the night.

Now that their feet were on firm ground, there were many important decisions to be made.

5

He climbed over the buggy wheel and for a few moments allowed himself to relax against the back of the seat, glad to be free of the noise and excitement, the handshaking, the questions, the congratulations. Undoubtedly he gave some thought to the meaning of this strange instrument, this rather frightening force he had loosed. The human voice, after countless centuries of use in making conversation, in delivering addresses, in singing songs, was now to be given wider scope. It was to be sent world-wide on chords of steel. When every home had a telephone (and he had no doubts at all that this would soon come about) the usefulness of the voice would be multiplied. All over the globe people would sit at the ends of wires and converse at great length. Business matters would be expedited, plans would be made quickly, news would be circulated. Perhaps in these few moments of relaxation he could hear, like the drone of constellations of bees, the incessant talk which he had made possible. For better or for worse, the telephone was going to change the face of life. For better or for worse! But he had no doubts, nor has anyone ever had since, that the benefits would outweigh the disadvantages a thousandfold.

He had given himself much to think about. By proving that the human voice was more than a sound produced by the exercise of vocal chords, he had taken the first step toward fearful and wonderful changes. Where would it end? Did he have at that early stage any of the prophetic vision which came to him later? Was he allowing himself to believe that lines spoken by actors, surrounded by contrivances more weird than anything conceived by Jules Verne, would be heard simultaneously in teeming apartment buildings and in isolated farmhouses thousands of miles apart? Had he any conception of a day when the voice produced in the throat of man would span continents on nothing more tangible than sound waves?

The sky had cleared and above him he could see the moon, surrounded by myriad stars. Would still more sensational uses be found for the voice in the realms of Time and Space? Would it be possible in some distant day to create echoes in the mountains of the moon by announcements spoken in whispers into machines in earth-built stations?

One thing was firmly in his mind, we may be sure. This venture he was making into the mysteries concealed behind Nature's Iron Curtain was a mere beginning and not in any sense an end.

Finally a very weary young man gathered the reins into his hands and began the long drive home.

Chapter Sixteen

The Summing Up

WHERE was the telephone invented?
There have been a number of occasions when
Alexander Graham Bell or members of his family have
made public statements on this point.

Taking them chronologically, there was a banquet in
1881 in Brantford, tendered to Alexander Melville Bell
on the eve of his departure for Washington, D.C., where
he planned to take up residence near his famous son.
Professor Bell had this to say:

> Every man desires that his name may be remem-
> bered even after he shall have ceased to profit by
> the recollection. I may confidently feel that my
> son's sojourn in Brantford will outlive my existence,
> because *under yon roof of mine the telephone was
> born.*

Perhaps in this connection I may be pardoned for
telling of my own experience with the great inventor.

I had the privilege of interviewing Alexander Graham
Bell on the morning of Friday, March 9, 1906. The city
of Brantford had planned a banquet in his honor. He
arrived the night before with his daughter, Mrs. Gilbert Grosvenor. I was a reporter on the *Expositor* and
so, notebook in hand, I was in the lobby of the Kerby
House as soon as he had finished his breakfast. He came
down at once to see me, a striking figure with luxuriant
white whiskers and hair. I asked him, of course, the
important question. Where was the telephone invented?

He smiled at me in the most friendly way. "I am going
to tell the whole story at the dinner tonight," he said.
"Will you be content with this much now? *I invented
the telephone in Brantford in the year 1874.*"

In the course of the memorable address he delivered
that evening (which I had the honor of reporting), he
said: "I have often been asked if Brantford is the home
of the telephone. All I know is that the telephone was
born where I was. Half my time I was in Boston and
half of the time in Brantford. This I will say: *The telephone was invented here.*"

Of all the public statements which Mr. Bell made on
the subject, this seems the most direct, the most fair,
and the most convincing.

Five years later, Mr. Bell spoke on "The Birth of the
Telephone" before the Telephone Pioneers of America
at Boston. This is what he said on that occasion:

And so it happened that in the summer of 1874,
during my visit to my father's house in Brantford,

Ontario, considering myself and discussing with my father the numerous experiments I had made in Boston relative to the reproduction of musical sounds by electricity *for the purpose of multiple telegraphy* [the italics are mine], the thought of the membrane telephone was elaborated. So that the conception of the telephone originated in Brantford in the summer of 1874.

On Wednesday, October 24, 1917, the unveiling of the Bell Memorial took place in Brantford. Dr. Bell spoke at some length and devoted himself to the part the city had played in the invention. He began by saying:

"I cannot claim what you know as the modern telephone. It is the product of many, many minds. All I did was to initiate the movement of the transmission of speech by electricity. It was initiated here." (Great applause.) ". . . I am very grateful for the assistance that was rendered to me in my initial effort on behalf of the telephone, both in Brantford and in Boston. A great deal has been said, and very truly, connecting Boston with the appearance of the telephone. Too little has been said in the States concerning the connection of Brantford." (Hear! Hear!) ". . . The telephone was conceived in Brantford in 1874 and born in Boston in 1876." (Applause.) ". . . You have two things that you can justly claim—the invention of the telephone here and the first transmission of the human voice over real

237

live wires. —But don't go too far, because there are those who claim and claim rightly that the first conversation ever held over a telephone wire was held in Boston."

B-24